START EXPLORING™

Audubon's
BIRDS OF AMERICA
A FACT-FILLED COLORING BOOK

GEORGE S. GLENN, JR.

ILLUSTRATED BY HELEN I. DRIGGS

RUNNING PRESS
PHILADELPHIA · LONDON

Canadian representatives: General Publishing Co., Ltd.,
30 Lesmill Road, Don Mills, Ontario M3B 2T6.

9   8   7   6   5   4   3   2   1
Digit on the right indicates the number of this printing.

ISBN 1–56138–638–3

Illustrations by Helen I. Driggs
Cover design by Linda Chiu Barber
Interior design by Frances J. Soo Ping Chow
Edited by Tara Ann McFadden
Editorial Director: Nancy Steele
Poster copyright © 1995 by Running Press

Courtesy Department of Library Services American Museum of Natural History, p. 7.
(Neg. # 335471 Photo by Logan.)

This book may be ordered by mail from the publisher.
Please add $2.50 for postage and handling.
But try your bookstore first!

Running Press Book Publishers
125 South Twenty-second Street
Philadelphia, Pennsylvania 19103–4399

BIRDS ILLUSTRATED IN THIS BOOK

American Flamingo

American Goldfinch

American Oystercatcher

American Redstart

American Robin

Anhinga

Arctic Tern

Bald Eagle

Barn Swallow

Belted Kingfisher

Black Skimmer

Bluejay

Bobolink

Brown Pelican

Brown Thrasher

California Condor

Canada Goose

Cardinal

Carolina Parakeet

Cedar Waxwing

Common Eider

Cuvier's Wren

Downy Woodpecker

Eastern Bluebird

Great Blue Heron

Great Gray Owl

Great Horned Owl

Gyrfalcon

Hooded Merganser

House Wren

Ivory-billed Woodpecker

Labrador Duck

Long-billed Curlew

Mallard Duck

Mockingbird

Northern Oriole

Osprey

Painted Bunting

Passenger Pigeon

Peregrine Falcon

Purple Finch

Rose-breasted Grosbeak

Roseate Spoonbill

Ruffed Grouse

Rufous Hummingbird

Shoveler

Snowy Egret

Snowy Owl

Sparrow Hawk

Swainson's Hawk

Tanager

Trumpeter Swan

Whippoorwill

White-breasted Nuthatch

White-winged Crossbill

Whooping Crane

Wild Turkey

Wood Duck

Yellow-shafted Flicker

CONTENTS

INTRODUCTION

Two hundred years ago, you could find me in the woods chasing snakes, collecting birds' nests, and stalking frogs. I was ten years old. I couldn't resist the call of the outdoors—and especially the call of birds. While I lived in France, I often played hooky from school in order to get a better education in the woods. My teachers never realized that I would become a famous artist and American hero.

Let me tell you about America and the beautiful birds that lived in its forests, swamps, and prairies. I'll give you tips about drawing and sneaking up on birds. These are important things to know if you wish to share my adventures.

Before I start, let me introduce myself. I'm John James Audubon, the greatest bird painter in history. Of course that's my opinion, but when you see my pictures you'll agree.

You should know that I was born in 1785 in the Caribbean, on the island of Hispaniola. I had a difficult start in life. My mother died soon after my birth. Four years later, my father left me to work in France. Eventually, he brought me to France along with my half-sister to live with him and our new stepmother. There, I received my education from school and from the forest.

As I grew, my parents wanted me to become a seaman like my father. I wasn't very good at that type of work, but I learned how to make great knots in rope. My stepmother hoped that I would become a priest. But I felt that my talents for hunting, horseback riding, and other outdoor activities were not suited for work in the church. Frustrated by my lack of interest in their ideas for a career, my parents sent me to the small town of Mill Grove, Pennsylvania, near Philadelphia. This saved me from being drafted in Napoleon's army. There, with the help of some tough Quaker teachers, I learned English and was able to explore the forests and farms around Philadelphia.

There, I fell in love twice—first with the birds of the new United States, and second with Lucy Bakewell. My first love inspired me to create the most fantastic bird paintings ever created. My second love, Lucy, supported our family and encouraged me to create the first artistically illustrated book of birds, *The Birds of America.*

With shotgun and paintbrush, I traveled over the American wilderness in search of new birds. Painting birds was not the easiest thing to do in the early days of the United States. The West was just a wilderness, full of Indians and uncharted land. The East had huge tracts of dark forest, filled with birds that are now extinct. I saw things that we will never see again.

Come explore through my eyes. You are going to see a lot!

MOCKINGBIRD

MIGHTY MIMIC

When was the last time you took a trip? Did you take a car, a train, a plane, or a boat? Today we have lots of choices, and traveling is easy, but in the 1800s it was a different story. Trips that take a short time nowadays took days, even weeks in the early days of the United States. You had to be tough and sturdy to survive. Travelers met with loads of obstacles. There were dangers of wolves, bandits, storms, and disease.

Audubon didn't have many of the items that make travel and life in general easier. He worked without electric lamps, aspirin, and, most important for working in the wild—mosquito repellent!

In this painting, a rattlesnake is threatening a clan of northern mockingbirds. Look closely at the painting. Do you see anything wrong with it? When it was finished, scientists said that it was not accurate for these reasons:

- Rattlesnakes don't climb trees.
- Their fangs don't curve forward. (Be sure to look closely!)
- Mockingbirds don't perch like that.

Who do you think was right about the painting? The scientists or Audubon himself? Well, score one for John James! He was a keen observer, and he knew about mockingbirds and snakes from a trip he made to Louisiana in 1821. Time and research showed that his painting is correct.

Rattlesnakes can, in fact, climb bushes. Some rattlesnake have fangs that do point forward, and mockingbirds will dance around in wild motions if an intruder is nearby.

Gray-and-white mockingbirds are found throughout the central and southern United States. They are birds with gobs of personality. They get in fake fights, they attack cats, and they love to sing. Their song is a wild mixture of their own songs and songs of other birds. Young males practice at all hours of the night. Sometimes they sit on the tops of chimneys and sing to hear their own echo. Of course, this may disturb sleeping neighbors.

In Audubon's painting, these mockingbirds represent the spirit of the new America. Just like the tough pioneers, these mockingbirds are brave, tough, and a lot of fun to watch. Since the Americans had beaten the British, they stood fearless against all competitors. This rattlesnake has met its match!

A rattlesnake is outnumbered by the feisty mockingbirds.

CEDAR WAXWING
"RED WAX" AND RED BERRIES

In 1808, Audubon married Lucy Bakewell and they moved to Kentucky. The trip took twelve days of traveling along rutted roads and across log bridges. At one point the carriage overturned. Luckily, only the luggage was damaged. Finally, they were able to settle in their new home, and Audubon started improving his skills at painting birds.

Cedar waxwings love fruit, choke cherries, mountain ash berries, and even cultivated fruits. Some people called them "cherry birds" because they rob the trees of the delicious berries. This habit made them a pest to many farmers. In the early 1900s, Vermont fruit growers tried to pass a law to allow the hunting of these birds. The law failed when bird lovers showed the actual bird to the legislators. They didn't have the heart to condemn such a beautiful bird.

During Audubon's day, cedar waxwings were a popular dish when the birds were fat and full of berries in the fall. Someone told Audubon that a basketful of these birds was sent by boat to his family as a Christmas present but they never made it—they were eaten for dinner by some of the passengers.

The cedar waxwing is amazing in coloration and appearance. These birds have a smart crest, a black mask and bill, tawny brown throat, and slate-blue wings and tail. The only spots of bright color are the band of yellow on the tail and the small oval-shaped red feathers on the wing. The red spots look like drops of wax. No other bird has these unusual markings. If you can guess why they have this pattern, you'll have solved a great mystery.

Cedar waxwings make open, cup-shaped nests from twigs, horsehair, twine, and grasses. Their nesting takes place late in the year in order to take advantage of the abundant insects and berries. During the winter, waxwings wander throughout the United States and as far south as Panama. Listen for their high, trilling whistle as they pass overhead in tightly packed flocks.

BE BERRY CAREFUL

Waxwings, robins, and woodpeckers can eat many different berries and fruits. Just because a bird can eat a berry doesn't mean that you can. Some berries, such as poison ivy, are harmful to humans if eaten or touched.

How can a bird eat a poisonous berry? Many birds are able to eat fruits that humans and other mammals cannot, because they have chemicals that deactivate the toxic compounds.

Plants depend on birds to spread their seed throughout forests and fields. To attract birds, plants produce sweet, juicy fruit. When a bird eats a berry, the seed sometimes passes through the stomach unharmed. The seed may be released in the bird's droppings. Everyone benefits. The bird gets free food, and the plant has spread its seed without any effort.

10

Audubon painted these cedar waxwings on one of their favorite plants, the red cedar.

PAINTED BUNTING
RAINBOW BIRD

In Audubon's day, America was thought of as an uncharted frontier—by Americans as well as by Europeans. For Audubon, it was a tremendous playground full of fabulous birds of incredible colors, sizes, and shapes. He spent hours hunting meadows and forests for any creature and plant that looked interesting. During these trips, he began to understand the rich variety of birds yet to be discovered for everyone to appreciate.

The painted bunting is one brightly colored example. The spectacular colors of this bird have no equal. Males have blue heads, shimmering green backs, and scarlet red feathers from throat to tail. Females are olive colored on top and yellow below. This makes it easier for them to hide while on their nests.

Painted buntings are related to sparrows, and can be seen in Georgia and South Carolina, as well as Texas and Louisiana. Audubon painted these in Louisiana. These birds constantly battle with each other during breeding season. The males sing clear, warbling songs from tops of shrubs and trees.

It wasn't easy for Audubon to sell his bird paintings. To make a living, he sold land, buildings, and he also owned a dry-goods store. Unfortunately, he was not a good businessman. One disaster resulted in an attack on his life, when his unhappy partner, angry about the loss of his money, beat him with a club. Audubon fended him off with a knife, and a judge threw the partner in jail.

Unfortunately for Audubon, he ended up in the same place. Because he was preoccupied with birds and art, he lost his businesses. Since Audubon could not pay his debts, he was put in debtors' prison. No one could have guessed then that this bankrupt young shopkeeper would one day become America's most revered bird artist.

Colorful painted buntings gather materials to build their nests.

YELLOW-SHAFTED
FLICKER

AN ARTIST'S DELIGHT

When Audubon was freed from debtors' prison, he was penniless and didn't have any references to get a job. The one thing he loved to do was paint. But he didn't know how he could make a living at it. Do you know what he painted? If you guessed houses, you're wrong. Audubon painted people. Since there were no cameras in his day, a painting was the only way to have a record of your family. With this service he was able to make a living and practice his true talents. His wife Lucy took a job as a governess for a local family. This extra income allowed him to continue painting birds in his spare time.

To see more kinds of birds, Audubon left Kentucky and moved to Louisiana. He found a position as a music teacher in the home of a wealthy plantation owner. He was very lucky. In the swamps and forests around the plantation he began producing pictures for his most popular work, *The Birds of America*. On the opposite page is one example—yellow-shafted flickers shown arguing with each other.

Flickers are very colorful, noisy woodpeckers that can be seen throughout the United States. They have a pink face and a gray head with a red band on the back. Their backs are brown like tree bark, but their feathers under the wing and tail are bright yellow. They have a white breast with black spots and a black patch at the base of the throat. When they are flying you may see they have a distinctive white rump above the tail. They fly in a swooping or wavelike motion.

Once on a tree they give off a playful *"wicka wicka wick"* call. They like to nest in holes. You can even build a box to attract this large foot-long bird to your yard.

This bird has many common names—golden-winged woodpecker, pigeon woodpecker, yellow hammer, wood pigeon, high hole, and many more.

NORTHERN ORIOLE
LORD BALTIMORE'S BIRD

If you follow baseball, you know that the colors of the Baltimore Orioles are bright orange and black. This bird wasn't named after the baseball team, but after the Second Baron of Baltimore, Cecil Calvert, who saw this bird while he was visiting Maryland. Several specimens were sent back to Europe, where Linnaeus, the creator of scientific names, described the bird. Lord Baltimore's name was given to the bird because his family seal matched the colors of the bird.

Orioles are really blackbirds, and singing and swinging are two things orioles do best. A male sings bright, whistling notes to keep others away from his territory. Females swing in nests that are shaped like bags. These may be made from horsehair, Spanish moss, grasses, and twine. The nests hang high from large trees such as the elm and tulip.

A cousin of the oriole is a South American bird named the oropendula (meaning "hanging golden basket"). These birds build nests just like their cousins. The nest looks like a swinging nursery with an opening near the top of the basket. Audubon, with his keen eyes, noticed that northern orioles make nests with more material than southern orioles. Why do you think they would do this? Audubon guessed that the birds from the north needed more padding to protect their young from the cold weather.

Males have black heads and backs. Their wings are black with white patches. They have an orange-yellow breast, belly, and lower back. A female has black wings like the male, but the rest of her body is a warm orange-brown color.

The female on the left is staying close to her nest. The two birds on the right are males.

SPARROW HAWK
(AMERICAN KESTREL)

GRASSHOPPER GRABBER

Audubon actually had a bird like this as a pet. The bird would entertain Audubon's family by attacking the family's pet duck. The quick hawk would swoop down and land on the back of the duck, which would rush off in terror with the hawk clinging tight.

Many sparrow hawks have been pets for young naturalists and beginning falconers. Falconers are people who raise birds of prey for hunting. The sparrow hawk is a great pet bird because it is easy to raise. These birds eat mice, other birds, fat grasshoppers, and other insects.

The color patterns of the males and females are totally different. While they both have a reddish brown cap with a gray band, males have slate-blue wings, a rusty brown back, and a black-banded tail. They're boldly marked so that they can establish territories and attract mates. Females, however, are camouflaged to hide from predators; just like the female painted bunting on page 12.

You might see this bird hovering over a meadow. A sparrow hawk has the ability to hold its position in midair so that the head stays in one place while the rest of the body flaps. Having the ability to keep its head still allows it to see field mice moving in the grasses below. Listen for the sparrow hawk's loud high-pitched call, *"killy killy killy killy!"*

The most common falcon found in the United States is the sparrow hawk, officially known as the American kestrel.

CAROLINA PARAKEET

PRETTY PARROT

The last Carolina parakeets were seen in Florida in 1920. Carolina parakeets once traveled in large noisy flocks between Texas and South Carolina. There are many reasons for the Carolina parakeet's extinction. These birds had bright green bodies, yellow heads, and orange faces. Their beautiful colors and energetic personality made them very popular as pets. Hundreds were captured and sold—young birds were taken from their nest holes and adults were trapped. Some birds were shot by angry farmers; these birds had a big appetite for many of the southern crops.

Audubon believed that the best place for these birds would be in the woods, away from people. There they could do as they pleased. Unfortunately, as trees were cut down for their lumber and weren't replaced, forests got smaller. The Carolina parakeet lost its habitat and wore out its welcome with the locals. Audubon saw these birds in the swamps and bayous of the south, but they were quickly disappearing.

In this painting, they are nibbling on the seeds of a cocklebur bush. The top bird is a female. Immature Carolina parakeets didn't have the pretty orange and yellow head. Their heads were green.

Can you find the young bird in this painting? It's the middle one of the bottom three.

WHOOPING CRANE

SLOW COMEBACK

The tallest bird in North America is also one of the rarest. Whooping cranes stand over four feet tall. All-white except for a red mask and black legs and forewing, this bird travels thousands of miles to and from its breeding area. Its route begins at Wood Buffalo Park in northern Canada and brings the birds through Nebraska for a short stop and on to Arkansas Wildlife Refuge on coastal Texas, where it spends the winter.

The whooping crane is struggling to survive. For decades its numbers hovered between forty and fifty individuals. Adults produce only one chick a year. Conservationists and biologists have tried to establish a new population of whooping cranes in the Yellowstone area. This program hasn't proved successful, but the number of the whooping cranes that visit the marshes of Texas has grown to more than 120 birds. Everyone is keeping their fingers crossed.

Many cranes around the world are faced with possible extinction and loss of habitat. The cranes have become targets for hunters in other countries because they're large and easy to spot. In the United States, the whooping crane is on the endangered species list, which protects the bird and its primary habitats. Many conservationists have become interested in saving these tall and graceful birds. In Baraboo, Wisconsin, the Crane Foundation finds ways to breed, protect, and restock areas with some of the world's rarest birds—cranes.

Audubon saw this bird attacking baby alligators in a marsh. The tiny lizards were being tossed into the water by the tall bird. With your help, we can keep these birds and alligators protected for Audubon's great-great-great-great-great-great-great-great-grandchildren.

This huge bird stands nearly four feet tall.

PASSENGER PIGEON

MILLIONS OF MARTHAS

Imagine the sky is dark, not because of storm clouds but because of birds—millions of them migrating from North to South. Audubon saw this and estimated that a billion birds flew over his head during a three-day migration. The air was so filled with pigeons that they covered the sun as if there was an eclipse.

Unfortunately for the passenger pigeon, it had delicious meat and was easy to find. During the 1800s, the business of commercial shooting brought down thousands of birds every year in order to feed people in the towns and cities. Most people thought the passenger pigeon was an unlimited resource.

Eventually, heavy hunting and loss of forest caused the bird's extinction. The destruction of the trees in the Ohio Valley took away many of its preferred feeding and nesting areas. In less than 100 years after Audubon's painting, an individual pigeon, called Martha, became the last known passenger pigeon in the world. She died in 1909.

Male passenger pigeons, such as the one being fed in this drawing, had blue backs and heads with orange throats and chests. The female, shown above, had drab brown plumage with hints of blue in the wings and head. Both had pink feet and white tail feathers with black central shafts. It is hard to believe that it was one of the most abundant birds in North America.

To celebrate the passenger pigeon, Audubon painted a male and female on canvas. This portrait was done in Pittsburgh, Pennsylvania, in 1824.

The vibrant blue and orange colors of the male passenger pigeon were amazing—especially if you compare them to the dull gray and black pigeons seen today.

LABRADOR DUCK

DRAMATIC DIVER

Audubon was able to document many species of birds that might have been forgotten without their true beauty being known. Even though many species, now extinct, were numerous during Audubon's life, he wasn't able to see all of the birds alive. The Labrador duck was one bird that he never saw, but was still surviving off the New England coast during his boat trip to Canada.

These birds survived up to the 1880s. Little is known about their habits. These birds were reported to be good divers that fed on shellfish and mussels.

Many sea birds and ducks, like the Labrador duck and the great auk, a penguinlike bird, became victims of over-hunting. Sailors who crossed the Atlantic grew tired of eating dried fish and saltless, hard biscuits called hardtack. When they landed in North America, they would raid the islands that were covered with nesting sea birds. The birds provided fresh meat and eggs for the half-starved sailors. Many islands were recorded on the sailors' charts as places to stop for food. Years later, when feathers became popular in hats and clothing, bird colonies were raided for the birds' plumes.

Some species of birds couldn't survive the pressure of continuous hunting and eventually vanished. These were the times before conservation efforts. Lucky for us, Audubon was there to record what is now lost because of human recklessness. Today we can look at the birds as symbols of the need to protect our environment.

GOBS OF GUANO

Many sea birds find that rocky islands are great places to raise young. The rocky islands provide protection from predators such as foxes. They also give easy access to seafood.

Great food and security allow colonies to grow up to four million. With that many birds, every inch of the island becomes covered with bird droppings. If the colonies are old, huge piles of bird droppings called guano (GWA-no) are left behind after the birds leave. The guano is harvested and sold for fertilizer.

The black-and-white duck on the right has earned this duck the nickname "the skunk duck."

IVORY-BILLED WOODPECKER

SHY HAMMERHEAD

This bird was the largest woodpecker in the United States. It grew to twenty inches long and had a clear, clarinetlike call. It lived in the large lowland and pine forests of the South. This woodpecker was one of Audubon's favorite birds.

Ivory-billed woodpeckers are very shy and don't like people. Those who have been lucky enough to see these birds know that they like to live in vast areas of forests filled with old trees. In their search for grubs and ants, the birds use their big bills to strip bark from pines or drill large holes into the trees.

Ivory-billed woodpeckers disappeared from the United States many years ago and were thought to be extinct. Recent sightings in Cuba have brought hope that this bird is still alive. Forest clearing in the 1800s kicked the birds out of their home, which made finding food very difficult. Research done in the 1930s said that only two dozen birds were left on this continent! Recently there have been reports that these woodpeckers have been seen in the mountainous forests of Cuba. No one is telling the exact location because scientists want to protect the bird from extinction. Maybe there still is a small number of these birds hiding somewhere in the United States—maybe even near your home.

If you live east of the Great Plains, you may see a bird that looks very similar. It's called the Pileated woodpecker. This bird is almost as big as its shy cousin, but it has a dark bill.

*Male ivory-billed woodpeckers like the one on the left have a red crest,
and they all have white feathers, black tails, and creamy yellow eyes.
Their feet are the same gray color of lichen-covered tree bark.*

CALIFORNIA CONDOR

ALMOST GONE

This is the largest bird in North America, and one of the rarest. Audubon didn't get a chance to see this bird soaring high above the mountains of southern California. Instead, he studied museum specimens and notes kept in museums and ornithologists' personal collections to paint this magnificent bird. In 1838, Audubon painted this bird with yellow bill, reddish brown head, and blue neck.

The California condor is a vulture. Like all vultures, these condors don't have feathers around the head. Do you know why? It's to avoid build-up of bacteria and dirt that could sicken the bird. Since all vultures feed on dead animals, their heads and beaks are working in areas full of bacteria, flies, and other messy stuff. If they had feathers all over their heads, they would quickly become dirty and filled with germs. The featherless head and neck lets the condor stay clean and healthy.

Even if Audubon had been able to see a live bird, he would have been disappointed with its small numbers. California condors need miles of territory to search for the occasional dead animal. They ranged from Washington state down to southern California. Today almost all of the birds are captured in order to help them breed to greater numbers. A few wild individuals were radio-collared and tracked electronically to find out why they were unable to survive.

These experiments found that condors sometimes get hit by cars and may get lead poisoning from eating buckshot in dead and unclaimed deer. Also, condors produce only one young at a time. These birds take many years to mature.

WIDE WINGSPANS

The California condor has a large wingspan, but it's not the biggest in the world. Its southern cousin, the Andean condor, has a wingspan of 9½ feet. Soaring high in the Andes Mountains of South America,

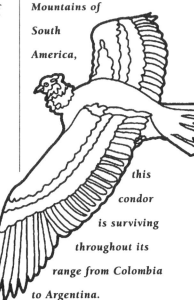

this condor is surviving throughout its range from Colombia to Argentina.

You can tell the difference between the two condors very easily—Andean condors have large lump of fleshy tissue above the beak and California condors don't.

Avoiding extinction is a slow and risky process for the California condor.
Fewer than thirty birds now live in North America.

BALD EAGLE

AMERICA'S FISH EAGLE

You've seen this bird on the great seal of the United States, on quarters, and on the backs of dollar bills. It's the bald eagle—but it really isn't bald. It has an immense yellow bill, white head and tail, and brown body.

The bald eagle is now protected in the United States, but it struggled for the first 200 years of the country's history. Farmers hunted this bird because they thought it killed young sheep and other animals. Little did they know, this bird eats fish.

Eagles live near water, but they are not fisherman. To survive they must find dead fish along the banks of rivers and lakes. Sometimes they'll even steal fish that ospreys have dropped. This is why Benjamin Franklin didn't want the bald eagle to be America's national symbol. He thought the eagle had a bad moral character because it stole from other birds.

When Audubon saw this bird on the Mississippi River he called it the "white-headed eagle." At first he painted it with a dead goose and then changed his illustration to show a catfish.

HOW YOU CAN HELP

- *Start by learning about the problems facing endangered birds.*

- *Write a report on your favorite bird.*

- *Ask your class to write your representatives in Congress and the Senate to support the Endangered Species Act that protects and saves all wildlife.*

- *Join a conservation society or an organization that protects wildlife. Turn to page 126.*

The bald eagle symbolizes strength and democracy.
How many examples of its use in advertising and corporate slogans can you find?

WILD TURKEY

BEN FRANKLIN'S CHOICE

The wild turkey appears as the first bird in Audubon's *The Birds of America*. He wrote that it was the "most interesting of the birds indigenous (native) to the United States of America." Today it is known as the main course for Thanksgiving dinner. In early America it was a prized food and a symbol of the richness and abundance of the nation. Ben Franklin thought the turkey would be an excellent choice as the national bird. How would you feel about eating America's national symbol with stuffing and cranberry sauce?

It was this great taste that nearly caused the wild turkey's extinction. As forests were cut down, the turkey was hunted and pushed to remote areas in Arkansas and the Appalachian Mountains. In the 1930s, the U.S. government realized that the turkey had practically vanished and began to restock America by raising birds that had been captured in the Midwest. These days the wild turkey is out of danger. Strict hunting controls help to keep it alive today.

Wild turkeys are very hard to catch. They have good eyesight and are difficult to see in the wild. In the spring, hunters use artificial calls to attract the birds. Sometimes a hunter will accidentally shoot a turkey vulture—and that's a big mistake! Turkey vultures smell and taste awful. Hunters can also be fined for shooting them.

This turkey is walking through sugar cane found in swamps
and riverbanks in the southern United States.

CARDINAL
STATES' FAVORITES

You've probably seen or heard this bird. Bright red with a black throat and mask, the cardinal is a strong singer and a favorite at bird feeders. So popular is this crimson red bird in the United States, that seven states east of the Mississippi River have named the cardinal their state bird. If you live in Illinois, Indiana, Kentucky, North Carolina, Ohio, Virginia, or West Virginia, this is your state bird.

Also called the redbird, the cardinal can be seen on many logos for professional, college, and high school sports teams. Few birds are as well known and welcomed as visitors to backyards and parks. Their loud *"cheer cheer cheer"* in the spring warms everyone's heart.

Female cardinals are not as snazzy as the males. Their bills, wings, and tails are red, but their bodies are an olive-yellow so that they can hide on the nest. Males and females sing in response to each other.

Audubon painted many birds that became state symbols. The second most popular U.S. state bird is the meadowlark, a noisy bird of the fields and prairies. Six western states chose this chubby, yellow-breasted bird as their own. Other popular state birds are the mockingbird (five states), bluebird (four states), robin (three states), and goldfinch (three states). Do you know your state bird? Check the list to the right.

STATE BIRDS

Many of the birds listed below are shown in this book. If your state's bird isn't illustrated here, go to the library, get a bird book, and find out all about its colors and habits.

Alabama—Flicker (see p. 14)
Alaska—Willow Ptarmigan
Arizona—Cactus Wren
Arkansas—Mockingbird (see p. 8)
California—California Valley Quail
Colorado—Lark Bunting
Connecticut—Robin (see p. 116)
Delaware—Blue Hen Chicken
Florida—Mockingbird
Georgia—Brown Thrasher (see p. 44)
Hawaii—Nene (goose)
Idaho—Bluebird (see p. 40)
Illinois—Cardinal (see p. 36)
Indiana—Cardinal
Iowa—Goldfinch (see p. 62)
Kansas—Western Meadowlark
Kentucky—Cardinal
Louisiana—Brown Pelican (see p. 54)
Maine—Chickadee
Maryland—Oriole (see p. 16)
Massachusetts—Chickadee
Michigan—Robin
Minnesota—Loon
Mississippi—Mockingbird
Missouri—Bluebird
Montana—Western Meadowlark
Nebraska—Meadowlark
Nevada—Mountain Bluebird
New Hampshire—Purple Finch (see p. 112)
New Jersey—Goldfinch
New Mexico—Roadrunner (*"Beep Beep!"*)
New York—Bluebird
North Carolina—Cardinal
North Dakota—Meadowlark
Ohio—Cardinal
Oklahoma—Scissortail Flycatcher
Oregon—Meadowlark
Pennsylvania—Ruffed Grouse (see p. 38)
Rhode Island—Rhode Island Red (chicken)
South Carolina—Carolina Wren
South Dakota—Ring-necked Pheasant
Tennessee—Mockingbird
Texas—Mockingbird
Utah—Seagull
Vermont—Hermit Thrush
Virginia—Cardinal
Washington—Goldfinch
West Virginia—Cardinal
Wisconsin—Robin
Wyoming—Meadowlark
Washington, D.C.—Woodthrush

In his journal, Audubon wrote that the cardinal "In richness of plumage, elegance of motion, and strength of song, this species surpasses all of its kindred in the United States."

RUFFED GROUSE
DRUM MAJOR

*T*hump. . .*Thump*. . .*Thump*. . .*Thump*. . .*Thump*. . .*Thump*. . .*Thump-Thump-Thump!* Spring in Pennsylvania brings the sound of male ruffed grouse. Males are trying to attract mates through drumming. Females like a strong drummer. Males do their best by selecting a fallen log for their stage. When they're excited they flap their wings on their chests to create a deep drumlike sound. The powerful sound is a sonic boom made by the rapid squeezing of air around the wings. The sound travels for miles! Females flock to a strong drum major.

With an audience, a male grouse puts on a great show. He'll fan his tail like a turkey, strut up and down the log like a rooster, and raise his black ruff collar to impress interested females. A good male grouse is as magnetic as any rock star and can attract more than twenty adoring females. The key to success is having a good beat and being able to wiggle your tail feathers.

Audubon saw many of these grouse during his travels in New York and Pennsylvania. They have always been popular game birds because of their delicious meat. Unlike many other birds, they have been able to survive the threat of hunting because they are fast and explosive fliers. Another reason they have flourished is that they produce up to twenty eggs per nest.

Because the ruffed grouse has many great qualities, it became the state bird of Pennsylvania. When you're walking through woodland regions in the spring, listen for the drumming.

DRUM MINOR

If you want to know what a ruffed grouse sounds like, make a fist. Start hitting your chest slowly and increase the speed. As you hit your chest, you'll sound like a male ruffed grouse. (Don't be surprised if someone gives you a strange look if you do this in public. It works well for the grouse, but not for people.)

Flaring their brown tails, two male ruffed grouse reach for berries.
A female looks on while the males fight it out.

EASTERN BLUEBIRD
A GOOD SIGN

Sky-blue singers of the country, bluebirds are welcome to farms and yards everywhere. Audubon watched how the male sings to attract his mate and protect his territory from other birds—even cats. Bluebirds sing a series of watery notes. Usually found on fence rails, phone lines, or exposed trees, they love open edges of farms and meadows. Only the smaller indigo bunting could be mistaken for this bird with its similar habits and colors.

During the last fifty years, bluebirds have had a difficult time surviving in the northern part of their range. They normally breed from southern Canada to Florida and winter anywhere south of Virginia to Kansas, depending on the weather. Many people in the Northeast noticed that bluebirds were becoming fewer over the decades. Their slow disappearance is linked to excessively strong pesticides used without care. Another reason is that bluebirds had to compete with woodpeckers, wrens, and starlings for nesting sites.

To bring the bluebird back to people's yards, a society was formed to promote the reintroduction and return of bluebirds throughout its range. The North American Bluebird Society helps people build nesting boxes. They band and monitor families and populations of these wonderful songbirds. If you wish to attract bluebirds to your yard, check out the listing of bird preservation societies on page 126 of this book.

While painting this bird, Audubon could never have realized the importance his paintings and name would have in the world of bird preservation. The National Audubon Society is working hard to help preserve birds like this one. With pastel and pencil, he was able to preserve the spectacular color of these sky-blue birds, as well as hundreds more.

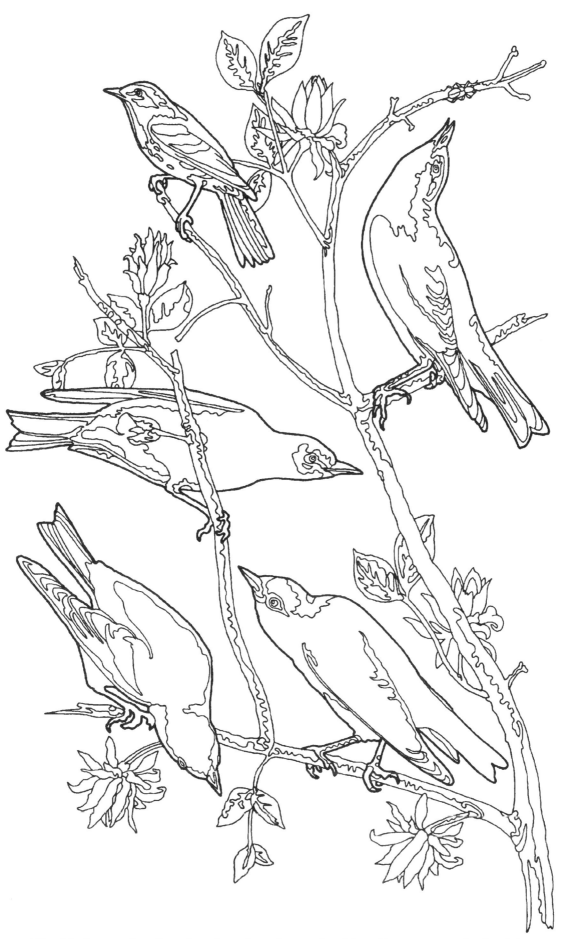

Bluebirds are closely related to thrushes and robins. You can see similarities in the rusty red breast of the adults and the thrushlike speckling of a young bird.

SWAINSON'S HAWK

PRAIRIE HUNTER

The Swainson's hawk is a common prairie bird. It hunts gophers, mice, and large crunchy crickets that some times plague the high plains. Found mainly west of the Mississippi during its breeding season, this large bird of prey flies to southern South America during the winter. Occasionally some will show up in Florida and other open areas in the East.

Adults are chocolate brown with a speckled or rusty breast, white belly, and yellow feet. They may be light or dark shaded, but they all have a distinctive white throat.

Audubon tried to picture birds in their natural settings. This required knowledge, skill, and patience to accomplish. Many times he needed help. He relied on a team of people to complete many of his plates. Since he never saw this hawk, he drew it from a skin collected by another explorer and naturalist, Dr. John Kirk Townsend. Audubon's son, John Audubon, painted the rabbit in this painting.

After completing the plates for *The Birds of America,* he and his family produced an illustrated book on mammals called *The Viviparous Quadripeds of North America.* Translated, the long title means *The Four-legged Creatures that Have Live Young.* Today this would be a terrible title, but it does make you wonder what the book is about. (If he used the same terrible title for *The Birds of America* it would read *The Oviparous Bipeds* ["ova" means egg and "biped" means two-legged] *of North America.* A title like that would not have brought many orders for his book.) Not as popular as the bird book, the guide to mammals features seventy-six animals.

FALCONS AND FLOCKS

Migrating starlings and song-birds must avoid capture from bird hunting hawks. One way to evade a hungry hawk is to dive into the bushes. The other is to fly in tight flocks. When a sparrow hawk is circling over a flock of starlings, the starlings form a tight ball of birds in flight. This ball moves rapidly as a unit. The hawk cannot pick out a single bird to attack. Also, the agile hunter does not want to get hurt crashing into a large flock of birds. Only the starlings that are able to stay together survive the migration.

Audubon liked showing birds in action—catching a fish, eating berries, or chasing away enemies.
This gives us information about the bird's habits.

BROWN THRASHER

BRAVE BATTLER

In a match between brown thrasher vs. black snake, there are no winners. The thrasher is very aggressive when it comes to protecting its territory. In this battle, one bird is tugging at the snake's back while another is trying to distract the snake. The snake is only after the eggs and has knocked out one of the birds to get at them. Audubon saw this attack and said that the snake got its prize—the eggs—but the snake was hurt so badly that it died. Sometimes a thrasher will give a beating with its sharp, curved bill.

These birds are terrific as neighbors, as long as you don't try to steal their eggs! They are found in bushy areas east of the Rockies. In the spring they sing wild, rambling tunes that are impossible to repeat and they shuffle through heavy growth looking for insects and fruit to eat. They entertain their neighbors and clean up the insects.

Brown thrashers look like thrushes with their brown backs and speckled breasts. Their long tails seem poorly designed for working in thorny tangles and greenbrier, but they move through the dense shrubbery with ease. Sometimes they are known as fox-colored thrush, sandy mocker, and red mavis.

Audubon had a lot of respect for these birds, and thought they were very courageous to fight a black snake.

The brown thrasher is related to the mockingbird.
To note their similarities and differences, turn to page 9.

PEREGRINE FALCON

BIRD VS. BIRD

Several birds of prey specialize in hunting other birds. The Cooper's hawk is known as the chicken hawk for its swift ambush of farmer's hens. The merlin, a small falcon, is often called a pigeon hawk because it terrorizes flocks of pigeons around barns and silos. The most famous bird hunter is the peregrine falcon. Its speed and size allow it to catch some of the faster birds on the wing.

Audubon pictured this falcon with a duck. Did you know that some ducks fly at 60 miles per hour? To be able to capture a large duck on the wing, the falcon flies high to scan for potential prey. Once a duck or slow-moving pigeon is sighted, the falcon pulls in its wings and starts a rapid dive. Called a stoop, the dive allows the bird to go as fast as 100 miles per hour. The unsuspecting duck doesn't know what hits it when the falcon strikes. Poof! Feathers fly and the duck tumbles to earth or is snagged by the falcon.

Peregrine falcons can be seen cruising seashore islands during the spring and fall. They surf the sand dunes on sea breezes in search of delicious shore birds. Amazingly, falcons also live in the centers of cities. Often they can be seen atop skyscrapers and on large bridges, like the Brooklyn Bridge. They have been introduced to urban areas so they can hunt pigeons, which helps the bird survive in a world full of humans.

You can recognize a peregrine by its dark sideburns, pointed wings, and narrow tail. When in Boston, New York, Philadelphia, or Washington D.C., listen for the high-pitched *"keck, keck, keck."* Look up and you'll find a peregrine.

FLIGHT SPEEDS

Hummingbirds zoom at 20 miles per hour.

Swifts migrate at 25 miles per hour.

Ducks cruise at 50 miles per hour.

The falcon dives at 112 miles per hour, but it flies at much slower speeds.

These numbers don't seem impressive when compared to the speed of planes, boats, and cars. But we can't stop, turn, rotate, dive, and fly through space like birds can.

This bird proves that getting involved can make a difference.
The conservation program has been so successful for this falcon that now its
population is large enough to take it off the list of endangered species.

BELTED KINGFISHER

OLYMPIC DIVER

If you're a beginning birdwatcher, don't try to spot a male belted kingfisher, because it has no belt! Only females have the rusty brown stripe under their wings. Males are slate blue with white throats and bellies. Their wing and tail feathers are black with white bars and spots.

Audubon wanted to name this bird the United States kingfisher. It's the only kingfisher throughout U.S. waterways.

These fisherman are the size of robins. They're noisy birds that clatter up and down streams in search of food or mates. When they're nearby they let you know by their loud call. (You can't miss it—it sounds like machine gun fire.) Then they swoop downstream and out of sight.

Kingfishers like to perch on dead sticks or branches that overhang fishing pools. They have sharp eyes to watch for moving minnows below. When an unsuspecting fish is spotted, the kingfisher zeroes in on its target and launches off its perch in a head-first dive. Splash! Its head plunges underwater and snatches the minnow in a split second.

Back on its perch, the kingfisher must turn the fish around so that the head goes down first. Otherwise, the scales and spines on some fish may get jammed in the bird's throat. This is a tricky move because the fish has a chance to wriggle free and may fall back into the water. (A kingfisher knows that dinner is not safe until the fish is safely in its belly.) With a quick flick of the bill, the minnow spins and slides down. Gulp! Dinner is served.

Kingfishers don't build nests like other birds. They like to stay near water, so they dig holes in stream banks. Females lay several eggs, and their young grow up in their tiny caves.

OSPREY

FLYING WITH A FISH

Flying with a fish that weighs one-quarter your weight is hard work! This osprey is well designed to catch the big lunkers. Known as the fish hawk, it hovers from great heights, dives, and plunges with a great splash. *Kerr-woosh!* If it guesses correctly, its sharp talons will grab a slippery carp, or as in this picture, a sea trout. For a bird, the hard part of fishing is getting back in the air with a wiggling fish and wet feathers. Their wings have unusual hinging that allow ospreys to raise their wings high and lift them and their prey out of the water.

Audubon saw this bird in New Jersey and wrote in his journal, "The largest fish which I have seen this bird take out of the water . . . weighed almost five pounds." He was so impressed by the size and ability of this beautiful fish hawk that he painted its picture in one weekend.

Ospreys are found near large bodies of water throughout the United States and Canada. The Chesapeake Bay is one of the largest breeding areas in the world for this fish hawk. There, hundreds breed on four-foot-wide stick nests built on channel markers, trees, and buildings. On the large platforms, parents raise two or three chicks on a diet of fish and nothing else.

You would think such a large bird would have trouble sneaking up on fish. The trick to its success depends on surprise and camouflage. The osprey's colors make it hard to see from below. It has mostly white feathers under its wings and belly. A fish looking up would have a hard time picking this bird from the clouds.

OSPREY RANGE

Ospreys are found throughout the world. When the young leave the nest they head to the tropics to learn the skills of fishing. After two to three years they return to their home territory to raise their own families.

During the 1960s and 1970s, ospreys were threatened by the pesticide DDT. Many pairs ate fish contaminated with DDT and could not produce strong eggs. With the banning of DDT and efforts by scientists to repopulate lakes and rivers throughout the northeast, ospreys are now reclaiming many of their traditional breeding areas.

Notice how the osprey holds its fish, with the head pointing directly into the wind. This makes it easier to fly to a nearby perch.

HOODED MERGANSER
MASTER FISH-GRABBER

Do chickens have lips? If you said no, you're right; chickens have bills. Do birds have teeth? If you said no, think again. Hard to believe, but some birds do have teeth! The merganser (mer-GHAN-zur) does. This fish-eating duck has a toothed bill that helps it snag fish underwater. Fish are slippery, but the hooded merganser has a hook on its bill to grab and hold its scaly food. Also, notice the large webbed feet. These help this duck to move quickly underwater.

On the surface, the hooded merganser looks like an ordinary duck—until it raises its large white-and-black trimmed crest. When it's near a mate, a male fluffs its head feathers. To really impress the drab brown-and-gray females, males suddenly take off, wildly paddling with their feet. Whoooosh! They race through the water, wings flared and feet flailing, in a rush of noise and froth. If you happen to be nearby, you can hear the watery ruckus. (Naturally, female mergansers always look unimpressed.)

The hooded merganser is the smallest merganser found in North America, ranging from 16 to 19 inches. These ducks breed in the northern United States and southern Canada and they winter in the southern states along the Gulf and Atlantic Coasts. In Audubon's day, ducks were a popular source of food, and sadly, would frequently be shot to be sold in markets in the cities. Most mergansers were able to avoid the hunters for two reasons. One, they didn't travel in large flocks. More importantly, their meat had a strong fishy flavor that was unpopular.

When Audubon saw these amazing birds, he used pastels and watercolors to paint them. This is definitely one of the fanciest ducks found on the water.

Audubon called this bird "a pleasing object to the student of nature."

BROWN PELICAN
MASTER SURFER

Do you like to fish and ride the waves? The brown pelican sure does. These large-billed fisherman are also excellent fliers. They have a unique ability to surf air currents that are just inches above the water. They flap their wings in short bursts and then glide along the air currents. Pelicans place themselves on the cushion of air that is being pushed forward by each wave. They can ride it without flapping their wings. Surf's up!

A pelican is most active when it's fishing. When it sees a school of fish it will flock to the area and execute a precision dive. One wing goes up, the head points down, and splash! When it hits the water, the pelican reaches out its long neck and opens its huge bill. The pelican's flexible chin and throat expand to create a bag that pulls the fish and water into its bill. This trick takes only a second for these talented birds.

When brown pelicans were most plentiful, they lived in colonies in Florida, Louisiana, and Texas. Audubon saw these birds in the Florida Keys in the 1800s. At that time, the brown pelican was in danger of extinction. People slowly wiped out its habitat, and waters became polluted. To save the pelicans and other water birds, President Theodore "Teddy" Roosevelt created the first National Wildlife Refuge on Pelican Island, in Florida. Now the brown pelicans are a common sight on pier posts in Florida and the Gulf Coast.

LOUISIANA'S BIRD

The state of Louisiana is proud to have the Brown Pelican as its state bird. After all, this is the sportsman's paradise—just ask a pelican where the fishing is great.

Adult birds have silvery wings, black feet, a chestnut brown mane, and yellow cheeks and forehead. The large lower bill sack is black.

BLACK SKIMMER
SPLIT-BILLED FISHERBIRD

This "fisherbird" is very unusual—it fishes without getting wet. Unlike the osprey or egret, the black skimmer doesn't dive or wade for its food. Instead, it cruises just above the surface, snatching fish with its bill. Look closely at the bill. The two halves of the bill are different lengths. The top half of the bill is called the maxilla (Max-IL-lah). It's shorter than the bottom half, which is called the mandible (MAN-dib-el). The lower half of the bill acts as a sensitive scoop as the bird flies low over the water.

Sometimes the long-winged skimmer fishes in teams of three or four. As they cruise over the surface, they fly a zigzag pattern with their lower bill in the water. When the bill hits a fish, the bird snatches and swallows it. Can you guess why these birds catch more fish as a team? What do the fish do when a skimmer passes over? They jump or flee—right into the path of another skimmer. *Gulp!*

Audubon watched these birds fishing the flat waters of bays and estuaries in Charleston, South Carolina, for hours at dusk and dawn.

When black skimmers are done fishing, they return to their nests or roost sites, usually a sandy or stony spit of land or island. Stuffed and tired, the birds are happy to rest. Adults stand guard to protect their nests which are merely shallow holes in sand or gravel. There, two eggs sit on the bare ground. The eggs look much like the surrounding rocks. This coloring keeps them hidden from large, hungry seagulls.

The skimmer in this painting has a white belly and black head, neck, and back. The wings are shaded black on top and white underneath. This makes the birds hard to see from above because they're dark like the water, and invisible from below because of their white belly. The only bright colors on this bird are bright red at the base of the bill and pink red on its feet.

No other bird fishes like the black skimmer. You can see these birds along the coast of the United States, from Massachusetts to Texas.

THE SKIMMER IN ACTION

When it's fishing, the black skimmer flies low, with its lower bill dipping into the water. When a fish hits the bill, the bird lowers its head into the water to grab its meal.

Audubon was impressed that the black skimmer could stay dry while fishing.

ANHINGA

SNAKEBIRD

This odd-looking bird is an anhinga (an-HING-gah). You can see these birds along the rivers and dark backwaters of Louisiana.

These birds are fishermen that need to dry their feathers completely before they can fly. When the anhinga is fishing it dives into the water and swims powered by its large webbed feet. It likes to eat fish, frogs, tadpoles, and other underwater treats. When it is searching for food its long snakelike head can be seen above the surface. *Splash!* The head disappears, then reappears with a slippery bluegill. After swimming and eating, these birds look for a sunny perch for their required drip-dry. Anhingas are not like ducks and other sea birds that have waterproofing oils. They need to dry their feathers before becoming capable fliers. Audubon pictured these birds in an everyday pose, with their wings and tail feathers extended.

Anhingas fly with their necks extended and their tails trailing behind. They soar like hawks over swamps and bayous from South Carolina to Texas. Adults grow to almost three feet long. They are black with silvery patches on the wings and neck and have red eyes and a yellow bill. Females and young birds have olive-yellow necks and chests but are black below.

These large fishermen are known as darters because their long needlelike bills are quick to snatch up swimming prey. They are also called water turkeys because of their big, wide tail. Compare it to the wild turkey on page 36. Do you see any resemblance?

The French inhabitants of Louisiana call the anhinga
Bec a Lancette, for its lancelike bill.

WHITE-WINGED CROSSBILL

PINE SEED PLUCKER

Canadian winters are pretty cold, and just think what they would be like without our modern conveniences. It must have been very cold for John James! In 1833, Audubon went to Labrador, Canada, to paint ducks, eiders, puffins, and other northern birds found there. The harsh weather made it very difficult and painful for him to draw—this painting took him six weeks to complete!

Shown in the painting are two males (bottom left and far right) and two females (top and bottom left behind the male). Male crossbills have a bright raspberry red head, back, and belly. Their tails are black, their wings, black with white patches. The females have the same wings as the males but their bodies are olive-green.

Look closely at the bill of the top bird. It's pointed and crossed. Unlike most other finches, which have heavy bills for crushing seeds, the crossbill uses its thin-tipped bill to pluck the seeds from the pine cones of evergreen trees.

This northern bird can be found in Canada, Maine, Minnesota, and the states of the northern Rocky Mountains. In years when the Canadian spruce and fir trees don't produce many pine cones, flocks of the white-winged crossbill and its close relative, the red crossbill, head south.

Pine seeds are a favorite meal for the crossbill.

AMERICAN GOLDFINCH

THISTLE DOWNER

The bull thistle plant pictured is a tough weed. Cattle farmers hate it because it pockmarks the fields. Hikers hate it because it's covered with hundreds of spines. Lawn keepers despise it because it's hard to remove from their carefully maintained yards. The only fans of this plant are butterflies, bees, and American goldfinches. They flock to these tall, spiny meadow plants because they're a great source of food.

After bees have pollinated the soft pink flower heads, the thistle sets seed. The flowers turn fluffy pale white. Then the goldfinches come and tear into the treasure trove of tiny black seeds. As they dive into the old flower heads, the white fluff is wildly scattered. Flocks of these twittering finches mob meadows of thistle in a feeding frenzy. They sometimes use the soft thistle down to line their nests.

Goldfinches have a very distinctive flight. You will often hear them before seeing them. They have an undulating flight pattern. The bird beats its wings, glides briefly, and beats its wings again. With every glide the bird lets out a *"ti-dee-di-di."*

While in New York, Audubon saw dozens of the these birds mobbing thistles along the banks of the canals. The American goldfinch has a black cap, black-and-white wings and tail, and a golden yellow body. The male sits above the olive-green female in this painting.

FEEDER FRENZY

Bird feeders are available in many shapes and sizes. Some small feeders are designed to attract small birds like chickadees, titmice, nuthatches, and finches. Plastic tube feeders have many feeding holes with perches. Platform feeders become covered with larger grosbeaks, bluejays, and morning doves.

All feeders attract squirrels and should be positioned on thin wire away from trees and away from the reach of clever squirrels. Large house feeders have bars that close the feeder when the weight of a squirrel is upon it. Go to your local hardware store and pick out your first bird feeder and watch the show.

You may see these canarylike birds in the fall, when thistles are fluffy white.

WHITE-BREASTED NUTHATCH

GOING DOWN!

"Ank, ank, ank" is the common call of this attractive slate-blue and black bird. The white-breasted nuthatch enjoys splitting sunflower seeds as well as scaling tree trunks in search of insects. These birds have a way of finding food that other birds miss.

In Audubon's day, the nuthatch was called the "devil-downer" or "treemouse." This bird searches tree trunks by going the opposite direction of other birds: down the trunk. With head toward the ground, this bird wedges its bill into bark in search of fresh insects. Meanwhile, its competition—woodpeckers, brown creepers, and chickadees—are heading up the tree and missing what the nuthatch finds on the way down.

White-breasted nuthatches are found from Canada to Mexico and will readily come to feeders. Their smaller cousins, the red-breasted nuthatch, prefer to breed in the cool pine forests of the mountains of the northern United States. Both kinds excavate nests in cavities of soft wood or bark.

Like chickadees, nuthatches will come to your hand for sunflower seeds. But you'll need to be patient; these little birds must become accustomed to your presence near the feeder. Start by holding your hand out with seed and see what happens. Don't be surprised when a bird tries to land on your hand.

CHOOSING BIRDSEED

Certain birds like certain kinds of seed.

Sunflower seed attracts chickadees, cardinals, purple finches, blue jays, and grosbeaks.

Millet/niger seed brings in juncos, sparrows, finches, and redpolls.

Thistle seed is loved by gold-finches.

To attract robins, mockingbirds, and woodpeckers, put out raisins, peanuts, popcorn, and suet (fat stuffed with birdseed).

In this painting, four males maneuver around a dead branch. The one on the thinnest branch is flashing his white breast and chestnut feathers at the base of his tail.

ROSE-BREASTED GROSBEAK

GAUDY NUTCRACKER

What's black and white and red all under? A male rose-breasted grosbeak, of course. The females look like large brown sparrows, but the males are hard to miss with a red breast, black head and back, and a white bill.

Grosbeak means "fat bill." Its beak is designed to crush seeds. Despite its powerful beak, this bird seems to prefer soft fruit and crunchy insects. Farmers see this bird as a hero because it loves to eat a hated pest, the potato beetle. As proof of this bird's contribution, it was nicknamed the potato-bug bird.

Others call it the summer grosbeak. Every year males return from their vacation in central and northern South America to establish their territories. By May, their strong robinlike song can be heard throughout forests from Georgia to Canada. It's often seen at bird feeders that are kept full of sunflower seed.

During Audubon's time, the grosbeak was captured and kept in cages. Reverend John Bachman, Audubon's friend, kept a rose-breasted grosbeak in Charleston for three years. Today, songbirds are protected by law. Times have changed, but this bold bird keeps on singing.

The pink berries of an American yew look good to the two males and one female.

WOOD DUCK
THE MOST BEAUTIFUL DUCK

Did you know that some ducks like to nest in trees? This spectacular duck is one of them. It builds its nest in holes or hollows of trees. It lives near marshes, small ponds, or lakes in woodland regions. Males in breeding colors dazzle the female. His bill is orange, his wings are an iridescent blue, and his feet are yellow. With splashes of pure white on his throat, bill, and wing, what female could resist such fancy feathers?

Audubon painted a section of this in 1821 while visiting Louisiana. Four years later he added the female on the nest. Many of his bird plates were painted in stages. Sometimes he would become distracted by other projects. Other times, he would wait for an opportunity to see the bird's nest or study the bird further. Often other artists added backgrounds.

Wood ducks range throughout eastern North America from southern Canada to the Gulf coasts. In the early spring they nest in holes of old trees. When young mature in April or May they must leap out of the nest and drop to the ground. Some chicks have to fall twenty feet. This is not a problem for the wood duck because these birds are well protected—their downy feathers and stubby wings help slow their fall. If that doesn't work, they bounce.

The female coaxes her young out of the nest with tiny peeps. When every fuzzy baby is out, she takes them to water where they feed on insects and marsh plants. This is a very dangerous time for the young. Below the surface large snapping turtles and fish are lurking—waiting to pull young ducklings underwater. The mother ducks are very busy keeping watch for other predators such as hawks and foxes, as well. It is not uncommon for several chicks to be caught and eaten.

On the right are the gray-headed female wood ducks, and the colorful males are on the left.

CANADA GOOSE
ISLAND NESTER

What does the Canada goose have in common with the bald eagle? It is a North American national bird—the national bird of Canada.

In the past twenty or thirty years this bird has become a nuisance. It breeds in heavily populated areas along the Atlantic coast. When a flock settles into an area they can make it very messy. These geese muddy the shorelines and leave a lot of droppings, which can damage ponds, by creating excessive algae and awful smells.

If you've seen geese swimming in ponds near your home or in zoos, you know that they're water birds. They like to make their homes on islands in lakes or slow rivers. Islands give them protection from foxes, coyotes, and other enemies. If a predator were lucky enough to get near these large birds, they would be sure to get a nasty reception.

In the spring in Philadelphia, herds of goslings (young geese) are watched over by mother geese along the Schuykill River. They're not very social birds. If you try to get close, some angry hissing goose may start attacking you. Watch out! At three feet tall with a four-foot wingspan, these birds are as tough as any attack dog.

In Audubon's time, the goose was a valued source of food. Like the wild turkey, it was popular for holiday meals. The goose, however, doesn't have white meat; its meat is dark with a very strong flavor.

"V"S MAKE IT EASY

Geese and swans fly their migration routes in distinctive "V" formations. Ever wonder "Y"? As each goose flies through the air, it creates a swirl of lifting air behind it. Other geese pull in behind the lead birds and fly as fast with less energy. Race car drivers use this technique (called drafting) to get pulled along by the lead car. They save gas and go as fast. Can you guess which bird works the hardest in the formation?

The most common goose found in North America is the Canada goose.
Most of these birds breed in Canada and migrate to the United States.

COMMON EIDER

DOWNY DIVER

E ider (EYE-dur) ducks are famous for their soft warm feathers that are used in stuffed pillows, quilts, parkas, and upholstery. Before the advent of synthetic insulation, eider down was considered the best. Down hunters, people who collect feathers for a living, would make nesting sites for these birds. When female eiders were ready to lay their eggs, they'd line the nest with their feathers so that the eggs would have a warm spot to incubate. The hunters would take the freshly plucked feathers, and the female would reline the nest.

Audubon saw these birds in Maine and Labrador, Canada, breeding areas for this species of sea-going duck. In this painting, a female at the top and male below, are charging at an intruding male with loud hisses.

Males are smartly dressed with a white head and a black mask and cap. During breeding season their bills are yellow-green and their breast pale pinkish yellow. Their belly, tail, and outer wings are black. Females are brown with black stripes so that they can hide in the grasses as they raise their chicks. If you ever get charged by a hissing eider, you'll notice its pink tongue.

Eiders nest on the ground in open depressions. They are vulnerable to attacks by foxes and other four-legged predators. With only a flat bill and webbed feet, they are no match for a hungry predator. How do you think they protect themselves? One trick they use is to raise their young near a resident security force—such as nesting snowy owls. The owls eat rodents, not birds, and owls don't like arctic foxes near their nests. Most foxes won't tangle with the sharp talons of an angry snowy owl.

Eiders are accomplished divers. When feeding they swim underwater more than 60 feet below the surface, searching for clams and shellfish. When out at sea, they usually fly in lines close to the water. A great place to see these birds is in Acadia National Park, Maine, where hundreds of eiders bob in the ocean off the rocky coast.

Beware intruding ducks! These eiders are protective parents.

TRUMPETER SWAN

GREAT WHITE TRUMPETER

This enormous and beautiful swan was struggling to survive in Audubon's day. By the late 1800s, populations were wiped out east of the Mississippi River. The swans were easy targets for both commercial and individual hunters. Because they're so big they had a lot to offer the hunters. Their meat was eaten and their skins were sold for feathers and down.

Today the trumpeter swan can be seen in Yellowstone Park, Wyoming. It likes freshwater lakes and rivers and has come back from a struggling population to a society of more than 1,000. The tundra swan, a close relative, had the same problems because it was a big target but is now doing well. It can be seen in small flocks in salt marshes and estuaries.

These birds are protective and ferocious parents. Their nests are built from huge mounds of grasses and weeds. The inside is lined with soft feathers. When their young (called cygnets) are ready to walk, they're taken to the safe water where they feed on insects and water plants.

The trumpeter swan has an immense wingspan of over seven feet. Of course, it's the largest swan in North America. Its feet and bill are black and the rest of it is white.

When swans were abundant, large flocks could be seen flying in a "V" formation. Their trumpeting cries were often heard even before they were seen.

COUNT YOUR FEATHERS

How many feathers does a bird have? You can probably guess that bigger birds have more feathers than smaller birds.

Hummingbirds are covered in a sparkling suit of less than 1,000 feathers.

Songbirds like robins and cardinals have several thousand feathers.

The large trumpeter swan has up to 25,000 feathers.

Feathers have many roles for birds. They insulate and streamline the body. They provide lift for flight and they help conceal birds from predators.

The beauty of the swan has made it a popular subject for legends and songs.

SHOVELER
MUD AND SCUM MUCKER

Hey Cow-frog! How would you like to have nicknames like Spoonbill, Swaddle-bill, Mudsucker, or Cow-frog? If you had neat abilities like the shoveler duck, you probably wouldn't care.

The shovelers have a big, flat bill that helps them to feed in an amazing way. When they are hungry they swim or waddle out to a muddy or mucky puddle, stick their bill into the water, and sift through the ooze. The shoveler quickly opens its bill and traps mud, insects, shrimp, worms, and algae. When it closes, the water, ooze, and other useless stuff rushes out. The plants and animals get trapped by a row of stiff hair along the edge of the bill and stay inside. After each mouthful of muck, the tongue snags the food and clears the bill for another load.

This male shoveler is a fancy bird that has an iridescent green head, like a mallard duck. His belly and sides are rusty red and his breast is white. Look closely at the different color patterns on the wings. They are sky blue at the shoulders and green near the inside edge. A white band separates the two shimmering wing patches. Females of this species are not as colorful as the males. They're brown with dark brown arrow-shaped markings. Their wings only have one bright blue patch.

Take a look at the background of this painting. The thick grasses behind the bird serve as a nesting site. A good site is very hard to find.

Shoveler ducks have very tasty meat. Sometimes they're called "butter ducks" because their meat will melt in your mouth.

The male shoveler (on the left) and female (on the right) are trying to reach a little snack before they have to sift through the ooze for their dinner.

ARCTIC TERN
WORLD CHAMPION FLIER

In the summer of 1833, Audubon explored Nova Scotia and Labrador, eastern regions of Canada. His trip was very successful because he was able to paint many of the northern species of birds during that summer visit. The sleek arctic tern captivated him. This bird is the master of travel on Earth.

In the summer the arctic tern spends 12 to 14 weeks raising its young in the lands nearest the Arctic Circle. In these warm months the sun shines for 24 hours a day. This allows the terns to supply their chicks with fresh fish around the clock. With all this food, the youngsters grow fast. By the end of August, the tern family is ready to head south—way south!

The family flies to the Antarctic during winter in the northern hemisphere. This trip down past Brazil and Argentina is over 10,000 miles. There they fatten up to return to Canada where they breed. The birds fly from the top to the bottom of the world, and back again. This enormous trip is over 20,000 miles. The result is that this bird spends most of its life flying between its breeding area in the north and the rich seas of the Antarctic.

This male has a red bill and feet, gray back, and black cap. If you wish to see one of these fabulous birds, go to northern New England during the summer.

FALL'S FRANTIC FLIGHT

Millions of birds depart south from Canada and northern United States to escape the harsh winter. Many birds such as sandpipers and warblers fly as quickly as possible to their wintering sites.

Their speed is astounding.

How many days do you think it takes a sandpiper to cover 2,000 miles? Only four or five days. That's fast. The trip is full of dangers— predators, storms, and ocean crossings. Less than half of the migrant birds make it back safely to their nest sites in the north.

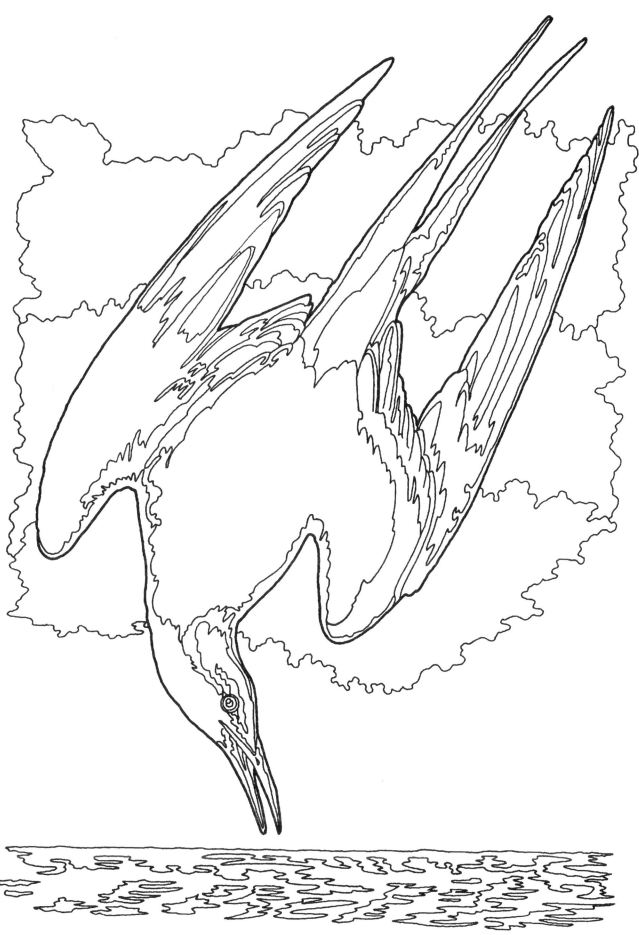

A dramatic mid-flight dive—a routine manuveur for the arctic tern.

BOBOLINK
REEDBIRD

Wow! This is one bird that you won't want to miss. The male bobolink is an incredible-looking black, white, and yellow bird. During mating season they swoop and hover over their territory while singing a wild song. Their song is a medley that is impossible to describe but very pleasant to hear. Of course they're doing this to attract females.

Bobolinks have many talents. In addition to flying and singing, they are expert migrators. In their travels, they don't make many friends. Can you guess who doesn't like them? The farmers, of course. Since the birds travel great distances they need a lot of food to keep them going. Flocks of bobolink swoop down on the southern rice plantations and raid the fields for seedlings or grain. This once labeled the bobolink as a pest instead of a master songbird. Because people thought of it as a pest, its name was left off the original version of the Federal Migratory Bird Law which protects most songbirds. Today the bobolink is protected.

In its travels from Argentina to Canada the bobolink has earned many nicknames. Hunters call it the reedbird because it can be found resting in marshes along the Atlantic coast. Jamaicans call it the butter bird, since its delicious meat was eaten in their stews. It has also been called the bob-lincoln, may-bird, and meadowwink.

If you live in southern Canada or in the northern United States near meadows or hay fields you may be able to get close to this yellow-necked bird. It will sing and sing for weeks on end. If you live south of the Mason-Dixon Line, look out for this songster as it passes through on its way to and from South America in the fall and spring.

The sparrow-colored female bobolink in this painting is just not interested.
This male (top) needs to show off in front of another bird.

BARN SWALLOW

MUDPACKIN' MIGRATORS

Many Americans note the arrival of spring with the arrival of barn swallows to their traditional nest sites. As the only long-tailed swallow in the United States, this bird is hard to confuse with any other bird. These small orange-breasted and shiny blue-backed birds travel to Argentina, Ecuador, or Costa Rica. Some swallows will fly up to 7,000 miles.

To get energy for such a long trip, they need to eat insects continuously. When they're near their nest sites, these birds can be seen swooping over fields and lakes in search of flying bugs. Sometimes they'll fly downwind of a lawn mower that flushes dozens of insects to them.

These birds once nested in caves and along cliffs. Now they use mud and grasses to create a large mud cup plastered on a ledge or eaves of a building. During the process of raising up to six chicks at a time, many black-and-white bird droppings plop onto whatever is directly below the nest. Their messy habit has made them a nuisance. Many products have been built to keep the swallows from setting up housekeeping in structures. Plastic owls placed in buildings work for a short time, but eventually the swallows figure out that the dummy is harmless. Large inflatable balloons with giant eyeballs that wink have also proven to be useless against a well-traveled barn swallow.

There is one place in the United States that really welcome these birds: the mission of San Juan de Capistrano, California. Every year tourists flock to this tiny town to watch the return of the swallows. The town sells T-shirts, caps, and postcards that picture the swallows returning to the town. There is even a song commemorating this event. To keep the birds returning each year, the town government dug a watery hole lined with mud, the birds' favorite nest material. In March you can join the celebration in California, or you can see these birds near a local barn.

Swallows need a lot of material to build their large nests.

RUFOUS HUMMINGBIRD

TINY TRAVELER

Zoom, zoom, zoom! Hummingbirds can outmaneuver any bird. They are fast and skillful fliers. All hummingbirds need nectar to keep hovering. (They get the nectar from flowers.) Hovering burns so much energy that they must go into a deep sleep at night. As they snooze, they lower their heart rate and cool their body temperature to save energy.

Just like people, hummingbirds need a balanced diet to stay healthy. Flies and midges help to keep them healthy. Spiders act as a source of protein. They are plucked directly from their webs. The webs are used later to glue their nests together.

Look closely at the hummingbird's nest in the bottom of the painting. You can probably guess some of the materials that are used—mosses, lichens, and small, soft pieces of plant fibers. The spider webs are used to strap the nest to branches or under leaves out of the rain.

Audubon never saw this bird in action. He drew it using specimens sent to him by Thomas Nutall, an explorer of the west. Audubon did see the ruby-throated hummingbird, a frequent visitor to gardens and feeders in the eastern United States.

The male rufous hummingbird has a dazzling throat with colors that can range from orange and red to purple, blue, and green.

AMERICAN REDSTART

SPUNKY WARBLER

It's May in the Blue Ridge Mountains of Virginia. The leaves of the tulip poplar trees are just starting to unfold, and the trees are filled with song. Dancing on the near-bare tree branches, a male redstart with black and bright orange plumage is singing *"tsee-tsee-tsee-tsee-tseeoh."* He is happy to arrive early at the nesting areas. Being the first may give this excited male the best chance of finding a beautiful green-and-yellow female.

The very active redstart is a member of a large group of birds called warblers. These small insect-hunting birds migrate from the tropics to northern climates. Redstarts are especially noticeable because they have bold markings and they jump, run, and flare their wings and tail feathers. Redstart comes from the word "redstert" which means fire-tail, so you can guess the colors of the tail of this bird.

In Audubon's painting, the male redstart is attacking a paper wasp. Notice the stinger extending from the tail of the angry wasp. Below the bird, a large paper-wasp nest holds the young that are encased in the paper cells. (If you ever see one of these nests, stay away from it!)

Many other warblers come to forests in the spring. Some have fancy patterns and markings, and others sing beautiful songs. Check out a bird book and you'll be amazed by the number of warblers that come from the tropics to nest in your backyard. The redstart spends the winter in South America in the jungles of Peru, Brazil, and Ecuador.

FAT IS FUEL

Airplanes need gallons of fuel to travel far. How can such a small bird travel so far on so little? The answer is F-A-T. For a bird, fat is fuel for its long trips.

Before migrating, all birds stuff themselves to gain weight before leaving for warmer lands. They eat so much that more than one-third of the bird's weight is fat. With that much fuel, the little redstart could fly over 1,000 miles non-stop!

Like many of Audubon's masterpieces, this painting was done in stages.
The branches were painted by George Mason and the female bird (top right) was added later.

TANAGER

DAZZLING GIFT FROM THE TROPICS

North America is very lucky to have three types of this beautiful bird. They are the western tanager, scarlet tanager, and red summer tanager (pictured here). The western tanager lives in the conifer forests of the Rockies and other parts of the west coast. The scarlet tanager can be found in the eastern forests, and the red summer tanager is found in the southern states.

All the tanagers have colors and patterns that will stop you dead in your tracks. Although they live in different parts of North America, they migrate to central and South America, which is the home of even more incredible tanagers. In Colombia, a country in northern South America, there are over 100 species of tanagers that range from dazzling blue and yellow mountain tanagers to the rainbow-colored paradise tanager.

Northern and southern tanagers feed on fruit and insects. The western tanager likes the California cherry crops. The scarlet tanager's favorite meal is caterpillars, but it also likes wild fruits.

Many tropical migrants, like the tanagers, may be struggling to survive. Deforestation (clearing the forests) and uncontrolled pesticides are hurting the birds. They are losing their natural habitats and are eating insects that have been poisoned by toxic chemicals. Conservation and protection efforts in the United States will help save land and protect the beautiful species found in our forests and prairies.

You might be wondering if you can do anything to help these beautiful birds. Of course, you can. To become involved, turn to the list of bird conservation organizations on page 126, and write them a letter. In the meantime, have fun coloring these brilliant birds!

Pictured against the green leaves of summer, three glorious red summer tanagers.

SNOWY OWL
ARCTIC GHOST

White with black spots, this owl blends perfectly in the open snow country found in northern Canada and around the Arctic Circle. In the land of the midnight sun, it is happy to hunt by day or at night. Notice how the talons and feet are fully covered with feathers. (Compare this with the great horned owl on p. 94.) Having fuzzy feet also helps this bird walk on snow. Only its bill is exposed to the cold of the arctic winds.

Large yellow eyes are designed to locate its favorite quarry, lemmings. Lemmings are fuzzy mice of the arctic. In some years when lemmings find an abundance of food, they produce many young, and their population grows. This is good for predators such as arctic foxes and snowy owls. More lemmings mean more food for the owls' young. Unfortunately, not all summers are plentiful and the lemming population drops quickly. When owls find that there is little food for themselves and their young they head south in search of other rodents.

During the years that lemmings are scarce, snowy owls cross into the United States. People see them along sand dunes, open fields, and airports. These owls are hard to mix up with other birds, especially when there is no snow. Because they live most of their life away from humans, they can be approached more easily than our resident birds.

In Canada, Audubon watched these birds fishing. One owl quietly waited by the water's edge. When a fish swam near, the white bird grabbed it with its sharp claw. Life in the arctic is tough so these owls will hunt anything when they're hungry.

EVER WONDER WHERE THE BONES GO?

Owls eat many mice in the course of a night. They swallow them whole—fur and all. After digesting the animal, the bones and fur accumulate in the owl's stomach in a tight ball like a cat's hairball. The owl throws up the pellet of mammal parts. Called an owl pellet, these balls can give you clues to what the owl ate.

If you are lucky to find one, dry it out and dissect it to see the tiny bones. Look for these pellets under trees where owls roost.

Two wise, old owls.

GREAT GRAY OWL

GRAY MAN OF THE NORTH

The largest owl of North America is a rare or infrequent visitor to the United States. When the populations of mice and lemmings decline in Canada, many owls head south during the winter in order to find a steady source of food. During this time the great gray owl has been sighted as far south as Iowa.

Unlike barred and great horned owls, this owl prefers hunting by day and dusk. Its large ears located in the side of the face can hear mice scurrying deep under snow. When it locates a mouse, the owl flies out and dives into the snow bank talons-first to grab the unsuspecting burrower.

Because these animals live in the remote woodlands and forests of Canada, they show little fear of man. A bird watcher can almost walk right up to the gray man of the north without disturbing it. When you get close you'll see the bright yellow eyes on an almost three-foot tall bird.

Owls are so successful at surprising small rodents because they are equipped for silent flying. Notice how fluffy and soft the feathers appear. Owl feathers are covered with a fine downy layer of barbs. This layer deadens the sound created by air passing over the feathers. Owls hunt with stealthlike technology in their wings.

Audubon painted this bird while he was in London. He most likely used study skins and specimens found in museums. When he produced this plate he wanted a mountainous landscape behind the bird. This was never added by the publisher. The result is a soft mottled gray bird with bright yellow eyes and bill.

OWL EARS

Hearing is an essential sense for hunting at night. Owls have a well-developed sound-capturing system that is built into their face. The flat area around the eyes is the sound-capturing disc for the owl. Below the feathers are large flat ears that collect and focus sound waves. This gives the owl the ability to hear the slightest rustle of a mouse under the snow. So sensitive is its hearing that an owl can judge distances from sounds.

Try closing your eyes and listening for sounds around you. Can you guess the distance and position of the sound within a foot?

Look out, mice! This great gray owl hears everything.

GREAT HORNED OWL

CAT OWL

The great horned owl is nicknamed the cat owl because of its brown tigerlike striping and large earlike feathers. Though this owl is second in size to the great gray owl, it's first in strength and bravery. Known for its deep series of hoots, this owl is a superb hunter that can take on rabbits, skunks, and many other animals. When it sees humans it usually flees for quiet woodlands. If you get near the nest of this owl—watch out! Many researchers have been badly hurt while trying to approach its nest. The protective owls won't hesitate to use their sharp talons on an intruder.

For many owls, breeding season starts in the late winter months. The males are responsible for establishing territories. Owls are poor nest builders and usually end up using an old crow's or hawk's nest. By February the females are in their nests while the male is hunting for food.

Everyone is familiar with the deep *"hoo, hoohoo, hoo, hoo"* of this bird. Females sing in response to the calls of the males. Owls make many other odd noises. One call sounds like the sound of a screaming baby.

Audubon drew these birds during the early part of his career. They may look a little stiff to you. Notice the somewhat dopey look on their faces. This is caused partly by the naive drawing and by the owl's sensitivity to light. One eye can change dramatically with changes in light.

While studying this bird Audubon almost lost his life. Getting close to these secretive birds is very hard. He found a nest in a tree swamp. While trying to get near the birds, Audubon stepped in quicksand. He was up to his armpits in smelly swamp mud in an instant. Luckily, his boatman came over and pulled him free. The owls must have thought this show was pretty funny. As you can see, field work in the name of science or art has its risks and rewards. Audubon had to take a lot of chances in order to get to see wonders that most people never see in their lifetime.

This owl has a very accurate nickname.
Compare the ears of the great horned owl to the ears of cats that you know.

WHIPPOORWILL

WAWANESSA

Have you ever heard the call of this bird? It sings in the oak forests, pine barrens, and mountains of the eastern United States and southern Canada in the spring. Its name comes from its sound *"whip-poor-will!"* Native Americans called this night bird "wawanessa." This bird is hard to find unless you flush it from its daytime hideout.

This sooty, black-and-brown male is shown flashing his white tail feathers. He is in hot pursuit of a fat Cecropia silk moth. The other moth, perhaps dessert, is a yellow Io with blue eyespots. The eyespots are meant to scare off any predators. This doesn't work too well when it comes to the whippoorwill. With the night's dim light the bird can't see the moth's spots. Gulp!

Look closely at the mouth of these birds. What do you see? If you said whiskers, you're right. The whippoorwill's modified feathers are stiff whiskers that point forward. They act as a net to guide flying insects into the whippoorwill's large mouth. The whiskers also keep the fluttering moths from slipping away.

A hungry whippoorwill chases down its meal.

AMERICAN FLAMINGO

IN THE PINK WITH SHRIMP

Do you know this bird? Have you seen it on lawns? Long legs, long neck, distinctive down-turned bill, and bright pink color make the American flamingo unmistakable. There are by far many more lawn flamingos than live flamingos in the United States. If you go to the zoo, you can get a glimpse of a live flamingo wading and feeding.

Flamingos are brightly colored due to their diet. Their white and black-tipped bill is curved down so when the bird places it in the water it acts like a flat spoon. Inside its bill is a series of ridges that are used to filter out algae and small aquatic animals found in salt marshes and flats of the Caribbean. If the flamingo is able to eat a lot of shrimp, it becomes bright pink. If it doesn't, it becomes paler. The flamingo is a good example of "You are what you eat."

Flamingos live in open salt flats. They build unique round mud nests that rise about a foot above the water or flat. The eggs are laid on top of the nest and the female folds her legs underneath to protect the eggs from overheating. Baby flamingos start out with short legs and short necks. They travel in groups with birds their own age.

BE A BIRD ILLUSTRATOR

If you saw an American flamingo, would you be inspired to draw it? If so, get a pencil, paper, and colored pencils, crayons, or markers and go to your local zoo. Don't start drawing right away. Watch the birds carefully. Notice their shape and color. Can you see subtle differences in each bird? After choosing one bird, try drawing its outline first and see what happens. This is how Audubon started learning to draw and paint birds.

American flamingos in the Florida Keys.

SNOWY EGRET
FATAL FEATHERS

Known as the heron with the golden slippers, the snowy egret is one of the most spectacular waders. The reason for this title is its bright yellow feet. The two-foot tall snowy egret has a unique way of getting food. It uses its bright feet to shuffle along and flush out fish, tadpoles, and insects.

The long fine plumes on its head, neck, and back are another striking feature of this bird. These birds are in their greatest glory during the spring when males flash their yellow feet and eyes at female egrets. Their legs and bill are jet black.

Not only are female egrets impressed by males' dazzling plumage, so are human females. In the 1900s, snowy egret plumes were very fashionable. They were used in hats, feather boas, and fans. The egret became a target of feather hunters and was almost wiped out. Eventually the fashion passed and conservation efforts helped save the bird.

In 1832, on a trip to Charleston, South Carolina, Audubon saw thousands of these birds in the marshes and rice fields, all in full plumage. At the home of John Bachman, famous minister and local ornithologist, Audubon painted the male in full breeding regalia. The background was not done by the master bird painter, but by George Lehman, a successful landscape painter. Audubon employed Mr. Lehman along with many other artists to paint scenery behind the birds. Can you find the hunter in the scenery?

Audubon painted this male snowy egret in Charleston, South Carolina.

AMERICAN OYSTERCATCHER

MASTER SHUCKER

Audubon had trouble getting close to this bird. He was forced to use a ship captain's spyglass to observe these birds from a distance. Then he relied on specimens which are somewhat different in color and pattern.

With a bright orange-red bill, white belly, black head and wings, the American oystercatcher is hard to miss on a beach or sandy jetty. If you're ever lucky enough to get close, you'll notice the unusual shape of its bright orange bill. It looks wide from the side, but is thin like a wedge or chisel when seen from above. The flat, wide bill allows the oystercatcher to crack open clams, oysters, and scallops and take out their soft meat.

Usually seen in pairs, these birds prefer to nest on islands and sandy spits. Their eggs are speckled like the sand and rocks and are laid in the open. Adults tend them carefully, but when threatened they hide the eggs' presence by walking away from the nest.

The young chicks run around on skinny legs and are very difficult to see. Their fluffy feathers blend well into the rocks and debris found on their island homes. You may notice that many birds choose islands for breeding. Do you know the reason why? On islands there are fewer predators to attack the birds or steal their eggs.

In this painting, Audubon goofed. He painted this male bird incorrectly. He should have painted the legs pale pink and the back dark brown instead of black.

In addition to the American oystercatcher, there are nine kinds of oyster-catchers found in the world. On the Pacific coast, the black oystercatcher, a close cousin, shucks shells from Alaska to California. The American oyster-catcher breeds from Massachusetts to Georgia and on the Texas and Louisiana coasts.

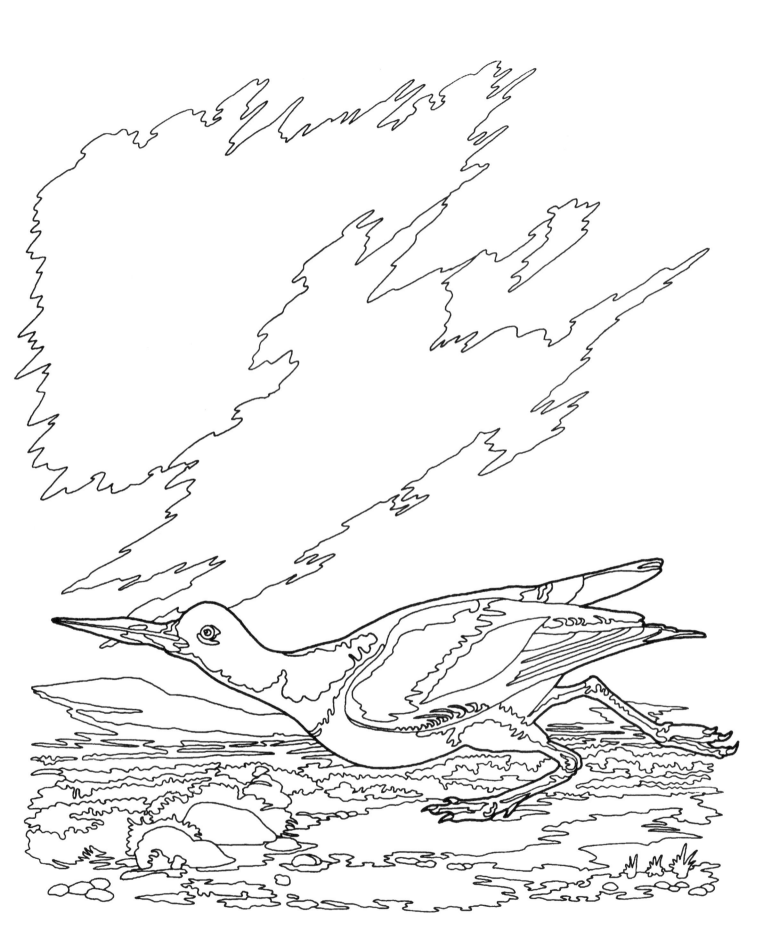

An American oystercatcher on the prowl.

LONG-BILLED CURLEW

NOSING FOR WORMS

Imagine how you'd look if a part of your face was longer than your legs. This is the case with the long-billed curlew. Its bill is almost eight and a half inches long. Its legs are much shorter.

The curlew uses its immense bill to probe the muck of the river flats. It acts like a long pair of forceps to snatch up worms and creatures that live in the ooze. The long bill allows the bird to keep its head out of the water and helps it to snag unsuspecting insects. Its feathers are mottled brown on top and white below. When the curlew is nesting in the western prairies it uses its snout to catch grasshoppers and other insects. This bird is not a picky eater.

In the background of this painting you can see the riverbanks near the city of Charleston, South Carolina. This part was painted by George Lehman, a landscape painter. When Audubon was visiting this city, he was amazed by the rich animal and bird life. He and his friends would sketch, fish, and also hunt daily. Whatever they caught that day was eaten for dinner. When they forgot the salt they used gunpowder for seasoning. In the 1830s there were no convenience stores to run to for last-minute supplies. People had to eat and live off the resources of the land.

Today, long-billed curlews migrate to western shores and are seen, only occasionally, on the east coast during the winter.

ROSEATE SPOONBILL
SPOONFUL OF PLANKTON

This tropical bird stands almost three feet tall. It's a wader like the flamingo and white ibis, but you'd never get them mixed up. No other bird has legs as long and a bill as flat as the roseate spoonbill.

The spoonbills have a unique way of catching food. As they wade through the water, their large bill moves side to side in search of tiny bits of food. Then the water passes through the spoon. The spoonbill's sensitive bill finds the food and separates it from the water. These birds spend hours straining water, muck, and scum through their giant spoon. Yuck!

The spoonbill has the same coloring as the flamingo. Its wings, body, and feet are pink. Its shoulders are almost a blood red. The coloring of the spoonbills and flamingos is a result of a healthy diet. The more shrimp and crabs they eat, the brighter their color.

When Audubon saw this bird, he worried about its survival. The beautiful, bright feathers were used in fans for elegantly dressed women of the day. Today the greatest threat to this bird is the loss of marshes and wetlands to development.

FILTERING BILL

You would think that such a large bill would be too big to catch algae and tiny water animals. The trick is that its flat bill is lined with tiny hairs that trap the food. When it gets a bill full of creatures and plants, the brushlike tongue pulls the food down its throat. Hard to believe that a three-foot bird lives on animals it can barely see. But remember, the largest animal in the world—the Blue Whale—lives on tiny animals too.

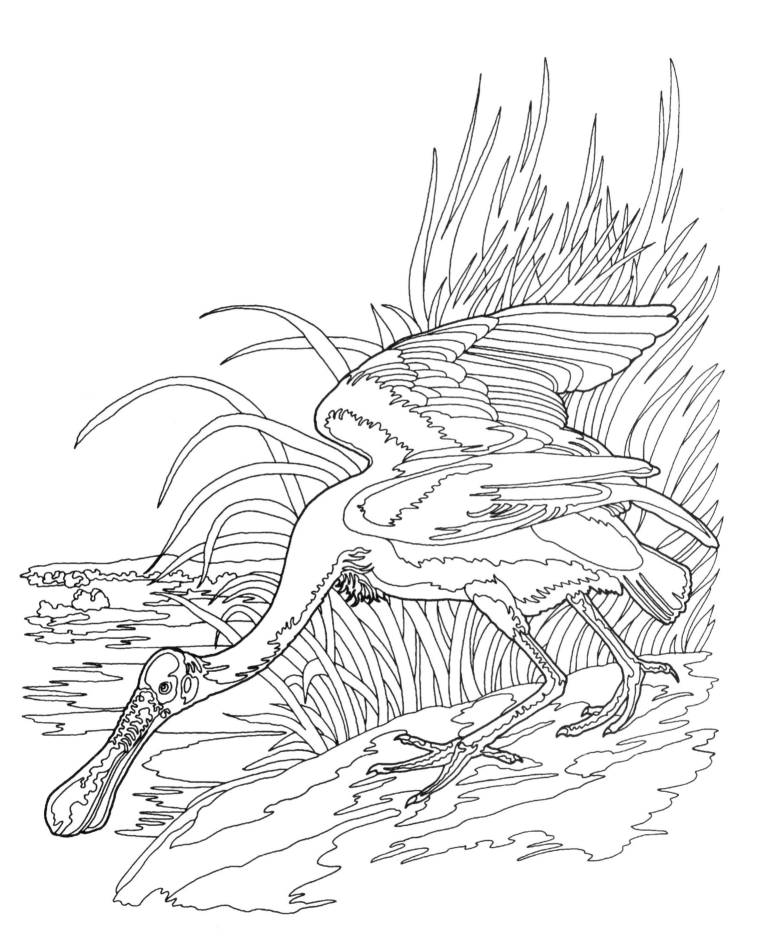

The roseate spoonbill prepares to fish.

BLUEJAY

EGGSUCKERS

These beautiful blue birds are troublemakers and thieves. The top bird holds an egg it stole from another bird's nest. Jays are smart birds that harass other birds and work as teams to attack enemies such as cats and hawks.

When they arrive at a bird feeder, they drive away many other birds and rapidly swallow whole sunflower seeds. Their obnoxious *"jay, jay, jay"* alarm call is well known in the forest and urban parks.

Their tremendous beauty seems almost unreal. The dazzling blue color of their feathers is matched by few birds. The color doesn't come from a pigment found in the feather. You'll be surprised to learn that the feathers are not really blue. They act like a prism that bends light and reflects only iridescent blue color. As a result, the bluejay's feather is really dull brown. As long as there is light the blue will never fade.

Audubon enjoyed hearing the sweet spring call of these birds. The blue jay makes a call that sounds like watery notes. When Audubon was in Canada, he wrote "The voice of the bluejay is melody to me. . . ."

If you like a cocky bird with a snazzy blue, black-and-white suit that attacks cats, feasts on eggs, and bothers hunters, the blue jay is the bird for you. Look for it at feeders and in parks.

WANT TO LEARN BIRD SONGS?

Buy a record, tape, or CD of songbirds in your area. Listen to them several times with a field guide in your hand. You'll start to recognize the distinctive calls of the birds.

Some bird watchers take tape recorders and play songs near a male warbler or robin. The mad male will come immediately to see who's invaded his territory. If the tape recorder is left alone, the bird may attack it.

Don't overdo this by playing the recording too much, as it may distract the male from other duties.

All jays have lots of brains. Their smarts come from being in the same family as crows and ravens, the well-known scholars of the bird world.

HOUSE WREN

TASTE FOR FASHION

This energetic little bird is a welcome sight to gardeners. The house wrens are quietly dressed in rusty brown feathers with black bands on their wings. Their song, however, is not so quiet. Wrens around the world are strong singers. The house wren will sing a bubbling series of notes followed by a burst of melody. The musician wren of South America can sing two notes at the same time, sounding like two harps playing together.

The scientific name given to wrens is troglodytes (trog-low-DIE-teez). This word means "cave dweller." The house wrens build their nests in holes and nooks in rock walls. They are very tiny, no larger than two inches tall, but very feisty. They compensate for their size with aggressive attacks on any intruder. Other birds won't even consider stealing a nest site from a settled pair of wrens.

The birds in this illustration have chosen an old hat for their site. Audubon said that he had seen nests in broken-down carriages, and others in old hats. If you leave your clothes on the clothesline, house wrens may come and put sticks in your pockets in an attempt to build a new home.

House wrens at feeding time.

PURPLE FINCH

PINETREE PRINCE

Male purple finches are bright raspberry red. They fly to tops of spruce and hemlock trees and sing with feathers fluffed. Females are more quiet and resemble brown sparrows. Finches are common at feeders and will sometimes arrive in large family groups. They especially like platform feeders filled with sunflower seed.

The purple finch ranges throughout the United States in the winter. In the summer, it prefers to nest in woods where needle-bearing trees grow. The house finch has become competition for the purple finch. This western immigrant was introduced in New York City in 1940. From there, it expanded to all of the states east of the Mississippi. Its original range was from Texas westward and southward into Mexico.

Purple finches can be confused with other purple birds that inhabit the northern pine forests. Get a field guide and look for pine grosbeak, red crossbill, and white-winged crossbill. Each bird has distinct differences. These differences are called "field marks." For example, a field mark for the purple finch is the all purple-red body of the bird. The house finch is partially colored in red. Some books have arrows or lines that point to the important field marks.

ILLEGAL IMMIGRANTS

Many birds have been brought to the United States as caged birds and then released in the wild. The list grows every year.

The European starling, English house sparrow, and European tree sparrow are the most well-known imported birds. Starlings were released in Central Park, New York in 1890. They are now found everywhere. In the state of Florida, pet budgerigars and canary-winged parakeets have been released and are now nesting.

New birds cause problems because they compete with local birds for food and nesting sites. Watch a pair of starlings drive a woodpecker from its hole. The starlings will win almost every time.

Purple finches are the state birds of New Hampshire.

DOWNY WOODPECKER

LITTLE BIG DRUMMER

Downy woodpeckers are fun little visitors to feeders, suet bags, and neighborhood trees. They make tiny squeaks as they hang upside down on a branch. They are mostly black and white but the males have a little red spot on the back of the head. Although they're the smallest woodpecker in the United States, they sure can make a lot of noise.

Each spring, male downys look for a hollow log or tree limb for their territorial recital. Excited by spring's arrival, males hammer wildly at the wood with their black bills. This is called drumming, and the sound can be heard for miles. With the advent of gutters and metal chimneys, downy woodpeckers have found that they can make more noises with manmade products. (Of course, most people don't like to be awakened at dawn by a love-starved woodpecker banging on their house.)

During Audubon's day, this bird was a friend to the apple grower. It would attack the insects that burrowed into the bark and fruit of the apple tree. Its one bad habit is that during the winter, these woodpeckers feed on the white berries of poison ivy. The birds bring the seeds to new places to make more poison ivy.

This painting shows a tree branch riddled with holes. These holes are not made by the downy woodpecker but by a larger woodpecker called the yellow-bellied sapsucker. Its way of getting food is to create a line of holes that will make the sap leak. This serves as food for the woodpeckers and traps insects.

LIVING IN TREES

Woodpeckers have many structures and habits that allow them to live and work on the side of trees. These special qualities are called adaptations (ad-apt-TAY-shuns). For example, an adaptation for climbing a tree is the strong feet and sharp claws. Another example is the stiff tail feathers that have hard sharp tips. These tips stick into the bark and allow the woodpecker to hold onto the tree while hammering.

Can you think of another adaptation for getting insects? How about the bill? Did you know that woodpeckers have barbed tongues? These long arrowlike tongues stick insects and grubs that are hiding deep in the holes of trees.

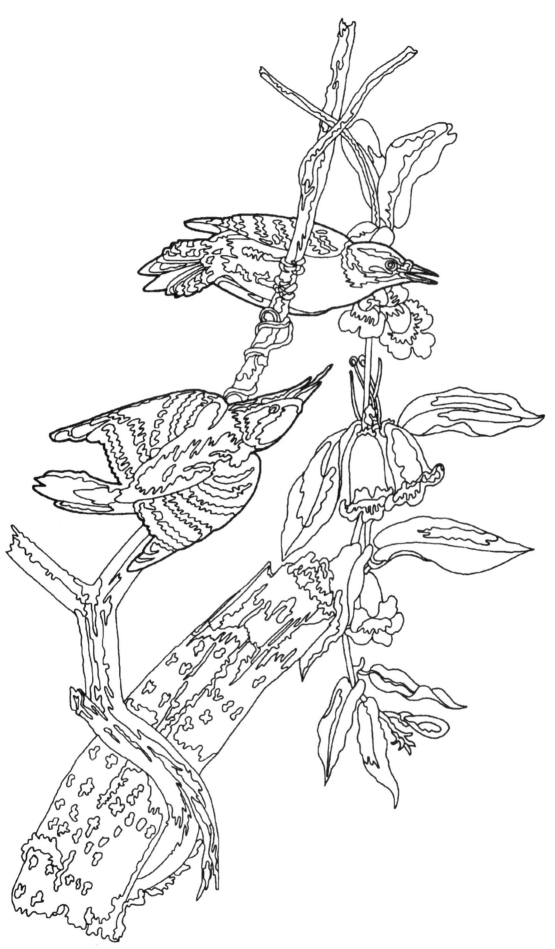

Downy woodpeckers make up for their small size by making a lot of noise.

AMERICAN ROBIN

NOT-SO-RED BREAST

For most people the song of the robin is the first sign of spring. Everyone waits to hear the robin's song.

Robins nest in and around our homes and yards. Our first exposure to baby birds is usually a young robin chick. When the first immigrants arrived on the shores of North America, they saw this bird which reminded them of the European robin. Naturally, they gave it the same name.

Robins in full breeding feathers have a bright brownish orange breast and black head and back. Young birds have breasts that are speckled. In this picture one parent is giving a plump caterpillar to the greedy young. The other parent is holding an egg. Do you know the color of the egg? When the young hatch, adults try to sweep the sky-blue shells away from the nest. This trash removal keeps the area around the nest clean and clear of signs that might attract hungry predators. This is why you may see bits of sky-blue eggshells in the grass during springtime.

What's the robin's favorite food? Everyone would say worms, and it's true if you live in an area that has a lot of worms. Robins will also eat a wide variety of insects and fruit in the fall and winter.

HUNGRY CHICKS

Ever find a baby robin chick that has fallen out of the nest? Naturally, you wish to become the parent of the defenseless little robin. First you need to find food. How 'bout some delicious worms? Next, how often do you feed it? A lot. Baby birds need to be fed six to twelve times an hour. As they grow this number can grow. Now, are you sure you want to adopt a baby bird?

Parents of nestling birds are constantly on the go finding food for their young. For large broods, parents must return sixty times per hour. That's once a minute!

Robins enjoy living in the open areas of suburban and agricultural America.

MALLARD DUCK
GREEN HEADS

Do you recognize the ducks on the opposite page? These are two pairs of mallard ducks. They're common visitors in the East at resort ponds and lakes.

To recreate that shiny green color effect on the plates was a tremendous challenge. With your crayons or markers, see if you can make the shimmering deep green on the heads of the boldly marked males. Try mixing green with thin silver streaks.

As Audubon traveled and painted, he realized that he needed to get his magnificent pictures in the hands of the public. People needed to know about the beauty of birds. Unfortunately, there weren't many publishers or engravers in the United States capable of reproducing his work. In order to find a publisher, he had to go to England.

With more than $1,700 and his paintings in his pocket, he took a ship to Liverpool, England, in search of an interested publisher. At his first show, almost 400 people came in one day. Audubon was a hit. Europe's art critics thought his paintings were fantastic.

He was invited to dinner parties and social events throughout the country. He told stories about his adventures to sell his paintings. Audubon was quite a sight with his wolfskin coat and long brown hair. Everyone recognized the woodsman from America.

Robert Havell, a printer, and his son accepted Audubon's work and began the immense job of reproducing 220 copies of the 435 paintings. It took eleven years to complete.

*In Audubon's day, these ducks nested on the small ponds
and prairies and farmlands of the Midwest.*

CUVIER'S WREN

MINOR MISTAKE

In 1825, Audubon didn't have resource materials—a field guide, binoculars, skilled birders, or scientists—to help him identify the birds that he saw and painted. There were very few people interested in birds when he was alive. One of the few men that knew birds was Alexander Wilson, a superb Scottish naturalist, who was exploring the country to study the birds of North America. Wilson was selling subscriptions to an illustrated book of American birds. He and Audubon met in Cincinnati. Wilson's bird paintings were not as elegant and dramatic as Audubon's. Wilson, however, was a better scientist. After their meeting they became rivals and accused one another of stealing ideas.

Audubon named this bird after his friend, Baron Cuvier. He should have asked Wilson for help. The bird pictured here on a sprig of pink-flowered mountain laurel is not a wren. It is a golden-crowned kinglet. It's suspected to be a rare hybrid of two birds, the ruby-crowned kinglet and golden-crowned kinglet. A hybrid occurs when two different kinds of birds mate and create a new bird.

Kinglets are tiny birds that live in pine forests of Canada and northern United States. They travel in small flocks with nuthatches and chickadees. Their high-pitched tweets can be heard as they forage for insects in spruce and hemlock trees.

Audubon painted several birds, like Cuvier's wren, that have confused scientists for years. Some of these birds have never been found in museum collections.

The golden-crowned kinglet—not a wren, as Audubon had thought.

BALD EAGLE

MAJOR MISTAKE

During a trip down the Mississippi River to New Orleans, Audubon saw this dark eagle with a light brown breast. He thought this was one of the most magnificent birds in North America. He called it the "Bird of Washington" in honor or the first president of the United States. For years he thought that this bird was a new species. But this eagle was in disguise.

Bald eagles get their white plumage when they are ready to raise young. This bird was young and didn't have the white head and tail. Audubon saw many young bald eagles along the great rivers of the East.

Audubon's mistakes were caused by his love and enthusiasm. There were few books and little time to do research, so he made the mistake of naming many kinds of birds that were already named.

Audubon's enthusiasm made it possible for *The Birds of America* to be published. Producing prints required the patience and skill of many individuals. Artisans traced the outlines of the originals on six-foot square copper plates. Then they carefully strengthened the lines with tools. After the sheets were placed on printing machines a black-and-white outline of the painting was produced.

When the print was dry, a team of colorists would painstakingly recreate the colors of the original paintings. Keeping the same color for each print was very difficult. At one point, all of the colorists quit because of Audubon's constant complaining. Audubon was forced to hire a new team to make his books perfect.

The proud and patriotic bald eagle.

GREAT BLUE HERON

BARELY FITS

Audubon's book, *The Birds of America,* was such a large book that it was called the Elephant Folio. It contained 435 prints. Each page was big, 29½ inches by 39½ inches, more than three times the size of this book. Life-sized images of most birds would fit on such a large sheet of paper, but not the great blue heron. To fit a life-sized, full-standing blue heron you'd need a book four feet tall.

These large slate-blue birds are common throughout the United States. Their powerful bill is used to snatch frogs, tadpoles, fish, and newts from the water. They have a five-foot wingspan. As they fly their feet trail far behind their tail.

When herons are startled, look out! They'll lift off with a loud squawk and drop their waste. This stream of stinking white poop is impressive. Such an explosion deters predators and lightens their load for a faster take off. When watching these birds, never get underneath them.

Audubon continued to struggle with color quality of each plate. He had to find money to pay the engravers and colorists. In the morning, he'd paint a landscape, or portrait. Then he'd go out and sell the painting. He did this every day so that he could raise $100,000 to produce the books.

Each copy of *The Birds of America* cost $1,000. Audubon needed to a good salesman, because many subscribers couldn't afford the high price. Audubon constantly had to find new buyers. Because of his persistence and love of birds, he sold nearly 200 books.

Today some original copies remain in private collections and museums around the world. Audubon's birds live on through his paintings which can be found in books, on coffee mugs, T-shirts, and CD-ROMs. The love for birds that flourished with John James Audubon continues with the National Audubon Society, which is devoted to the conservation of birds and their habitats throughout the world.

This bird had to be drawn bent over to fit on the pages of THE BIRDS OF AMERICA.

GYRFALCON
TERROR FOR PTARMIGANS

Gyrfalcon (JER-fal-con) means "noble falcon." It's the largest falcon in North America. All white with black spots and yellow feet, this arctic hunter nests on cliffs. Its favorite foods are other birds such as the ptarmigan (TAR-me-ghan), an arctic grouse. Audubon observed gyrfalcons in Labrador as they chased sea birds that nested in the rocks.

Would you like to watch these large white falcons wheeling over cliffs? Does witnessing the splashy fishing dive of an osprey interest you? Do the mysterious hoots of an owl make you wonder what it looks like or where it lives? If yes is your answer, borrow a book, build a bird feeder, and start your adventure. Most importantly, have fun . . . Audubon did!

FOR FURTHER READING
FIELD GUIDES

The Bird Feeder Book. Stokes Backyard Nature Series. Boston: Little Brown, 1987.

Birdwatching for All Ages, Activities for Children and Adults.
Jorie Hunken. Old Saybrook, Connecticut: Globe Pequot Press, 1992.

Eastern Birds. Roger Tory Peterson. New York: Houghton Mifflin, 1980.

Field Guide to the Birds of North America. National Geographic Society. Washington, D.C.: 1987.

National Audubon Society Field Guide to North American Birds. New York: Chanticleer Press, 1994.

Western Birds. Roger Tory Peterson. New York: Houghton Mifflin, 1990.

Peterson's First Guide to Birds. New York: Houghton Mifflin, 1986.

BIRD SONGS

Know Your Bird Sounds. Elliott Lang. Ithaca, New York: Nature Sound Studio, 1991.

ATTRACTING BIRDS

Birdscaping Your Garden: Landscaping and Planting for Birds. George Adams. Emmaus, Pennsylvania: Rodale Press, 1994.

The Complete Bird House Book. D & L Stokes. Boston: Little, Brown & Company, 1990.

Feed the Birds. Helen and Dick Witty. New York: Workman, 1991.

ORGANIZATIONS

American Birding Association. Bird's Eye View, P. O. Box 659, Colorado Springs, CO 80934
Write for a newsletter and learn about bird programs for all ages.

National Audubon Society, 700 Broadway, New York, NY 10003
Write to find your nearest local chapter.

North American Bluebird Society, Box 6295, Silver Spring, MD 20906
Write for a newsletter to help save bluebirds.

Project Feeder Watch. Cornell Lab of Ornithology, P. O. Box 11, Ithaca, NY 14851–0011
Participate in a national study of feeder birds.

RARE Center for Tropical Bird Conservation, 1616 Walnut Street, Suite 911, Philadelphia, PA 11903
Help children and young adults in other countries protect their spectacular birds.

A gyrfalcon at work.

COLOR YOUR WORLD

With crayons, markers and imagination, you can re-create works of art and discover the worlds of science, nature, and literature. Each book is $8.95 and is available from your local bookstore. If your bookstore does not have the volume you want, ask your bookseller to order it for you (or send a check/money order for the cost of each book plus $2.50 postage and handling to Running Press).

THE AGE OF DINOSAURS
by Donald F. Glut

Discover new theories about dinosaurs and learn how paleontologists work in this fascinating expedition to a time when reptiles ruled the land.

THE AMERICAN WEST
by Emmanuel M. Kramer

Explore the lives and legends of the American West—with 60 images to color.

ARCHITECTURE
by Peter Dobrin

Tour 60 world-famous buildings around the world and learn their stories.

BULFINCH'S MYTHOLOGY
Retold by Steven Zorn

An excellent introduction to classical literature, with 16 tales of adventure.

FOLKTALES OF NATIVE AMERICANS
Retold by David Borgenicht

Traditional myths, tales, and legends, from more than 12 Native American peoples.

FORESTS
by Elizabeth Corning Dudley, Ph.D.

Winner, Parents' Choice
"Learning and Doing Award"
The first ecological coloring book, written by a respected botanist.

GRAY'S ANATOMY
by Fred Stark, Ph.D.

Winner, Parents' Choice
"Learning and Doing Award"
A voyage of discovery through the human body, based on the classic work.

INSECTS
by George S. Glenn, Jr.

Discover the secrets of familiar and more unusual insects.

MASTERPIECES
by Mary Martin and Steven Zorn

Line drawings and lively descriptions of 60 world-famous paintings and their artists.

OCEANS
by Diane M. Tyler and James C. Tyler, Ph.D.

Winner, Parents' Choice
"Learning and Doing Award"
An exploration of the life-giving seas, in expert text and 60 pictures.

PLACES OF MYSTERY
by Emmanuel M. Kramer

An adventurous tour of the most mysterious places on Earth, with more than 50 stops along the way.

SPACE
by Dennis Mammana

Share the discoveries of history's greatest space scientists and explorers.